GW00385154

# The Structures and Properties of Solids
a series of student texts

*General Editor:*
Professor Bryan R. Coles

The Structures and Properties of Solids 6

# The Magnetic Properties of Solids

## J. Crangle

Reader in Physics, University of Sheffield

Edward Arnold

© J. Crangle 1977

First published 1977 by Edward Arnold (Publishers) Limited
25 Hill Street, London W1X 8LL

Boards Edition  ISBN: 0 7131 2573 X
Paper Edition:  ISBN: 0 7131 2574 8

All rights reserved. No part of this publication
may be reproduced, stored in a retrieval
system, or transmitted in any form or by any
means, electronic, mechanical, photocopying,
recording or otherwise, without the prior
permission of Edward Arnold (Publishers)
Limited.

Printed in Great Britain by
Willmer Brothers Limited, Merseyside.

# General Editor's Preface

Of all the electronic properties of solids magnetism is perhaps that of interest or concern to the widest range of scientists and technologists. At one extreme, quite small improvements in permeability or saturation magnetization can be of great economic significance to the engineer; at the other, magnetic phase transitions have supplied the model systems for some of the most abstract recent discussion of theoretical physicists. The very existence of the most striking form of magnetism—ferromagnetism— has provided generations of students with a stimulating oddity and confronts the solid state physicist with one of his most natural questions. 'Why is iron ferromagnetic?' belongs with 'Why is aluminium a conductor and diamond an insulator?' and 'Why is steel stronger than copper?' as one of the central questions posed by our everyday experience of solids. It is impossible to cover the whole range of magnetic phenomena and satisfy all interested parties in one book; the author has taken a clear decision to make the focus of his book the bulk magnetic properties of solid materials, their explanation in atomic terms and their applications. In this decision, as in the straightforwardness of his explanations and the obvious relish he has for the experimental challenges and pleasures the topic affords, Dr Crangle shows himself to be in the central tradition established by such pioneers of the subject as his teacher Professor W. Sucksmith and Professor L. F. Bates. In another respect however he breaks new ground by providing the first consistent textbook treatment of magnetism as a branch of solid state physics wholly in SI units. The many students who have found difficulty in reconciling their studies of magnetism in solids with their wholly SI based treatment of formal electricity and magnetism will be deeply grateful.

Imperial College
London,
1977

BRC

# Preface

The magnetic properties of solids are important and they vary widely. Attempts to understand them have led to a deep insight into the fundamental structure of many different metallic or non-metallic solids, although this understanding is often still far from complete. In addition to the fundamental interest in their magnetic properties there is a large and growing technology based on the applications of the properties of magnetic materials.

The aim of this book is to provide a simple introduction to the study of solid state magnetism, both intrinsic and technical. The level of the treatment is that of a senior undergraduate studying physics in a British university. It is hoped that the book will also meet the needs of a wider group than this, such as chemists, electrical engineers, metallurgists and materials scientists, some at a postgraduate level; or practising scientists specializing in other areas who require an introduction to magnetism.

The subject matter is treated selectively rather than comprehensively and the size of the book is limited so that those who are studying several other topics simultaneously may grasp most of the contents fairly easily. The treatment is experimental and descriptive, with an accent on the basic principles involved. The list of references and suggestions for further reading should help the reader to find fuller and deeper accounts of various parts of magnetism when he is ready to deal with them. Perhaps the most outstanding of the important topics omitted is magnetic resonance, except where it is used to measure applied magnetic fields or hyperfine fields. Experiments employing inelastic scattering of neutrons are not discussed, nor are spin waves. Also the newly discovered properties connected with limited dimensionality and materials called spin glasses or mictomagnets are left out.

The system of units used is SI. Wherever possible quantities are given also in CGS electromagnetic units. No choice is made between the Sommerfeld and the Kennelly systems of magnetic units but a distinctive nomenclature is employed which should enable either to be used where appropriate and ambiguity to be avoided. Susceptibilities are so defined that conversion between SI and CGS only requires movement of the decimal point.

Sheffield                                                                JC
1976

# Contents

x    CONTENTS

# Index of Symbols

# 1

# Introduction and Survey
# of Basic Experimental Properties

The magnetic properties of solids are important and attempts to understand them have led to a deep insight into the fundamental structure of many solids, both metallic and non-metallic. However, in many cases the understanding is still far from complete. As in other areas of science the need to test theories that have themselves been set up to explain and correlate previous experimental information has suggested new experimental approaches. These have led to further theoretical development, and so on. In magnetism the process has been accelerated particularly by the recent development of several completely new experimental techniques. A very wide variety of magnetic behaviour has now been recognized in hundreds of different materials. One of the problems in magnetism is that there are serious mathematical difficulties in tackling parts of the subject with theories that are very realistic. Furthermore, it has not yet been possible in many areas to devise sufficiently sensitive experiments to test theoretical predictions and so to give an indication of which among diverging branches in a theory is correct. On the other hand, theoretical models based on one-dimensional or two-dimensional simplifications have sometimes been treated and major distortions of the theory due to the simplification have been found. But the range of available magnetic materials produced both by metallurgy and by chemistry is so very large that examples have often been found experimentally which satisfy the conditions of the simplified theory, often verifying it in a remarkable way.

In addition to the fundamental interest in the magnetic properties of solids there is a great interest in the applications of magnetic materials. There has grown up a tendency to divide magnetism into two kinds. The first is called intrinsic magnetism, concerned with relating magnetic properties to electronic structure and other fundamentals in metals or non-metals. The second, technical magnetism, which is a large subject in itself, is concerned largely with the properties of magnetic domains and related phenomena. Of course, there is quite a lot of cross coupling between the two groups.

The aim of this book is to provide a simple introduction to magnetism in solids, both intrinsic magnetism and technical magnetism. The level of the treatment is intended to be that of a senior undergraduate studying physics in a British university, although it can meet the needs of a wider group than this. The treatment is experimental and descriptive, with an accent on the basic principles involved. The rest of this first chapter is devoted mainly to an outline of the more obvious experimental magnetic properties, to highlight the needs for the explanations which follow.

## 1.1  Basic magnetic properties

That lodestone (magnetite, $Fe_3O_4$), a natural non-metallic solid, may attract iron was first described in known Greek writings about 800 B.C. But the scientific significance was not appreciated until some time later. This was the first technical magnetic material because it formed the first compass.

### 1.1.1  *Ferromagnetic materials*

The most widely recognized magnetic elements are iron, nickel and cobalt. These are all ferromagnetic, that is they possess atomic magnetic moments which are ordered (aligned) below some critical temperature. The most obvious properties of a ferromagnet are as follows.

If a piece of iron is examined at room temperature it may be obtained first in an unmagnetized state. If it is then placed in a relatively weak magnetic field a magnetic moment is induced. Such a field may be produced by wrapping a few turns of wire round the iron specimen and passing an electric current of the order of one ampere through it, or by placing the specimen in the vicinity of another specimen which is permanently magnetized. The magnetic state of the iron specimen depends on the magnetic field in a relatively complicated way. There are also differences in the definition of the magnetic state according to how it is measured. The different measuring techniques are described in Chapter 7. The magnetization is given by a measurement depending on the dipole moment of the specimen, for example the measurement of the change in field at some point outside the specimen due to the presence of the specimen. Otherwise the induction within the specimen can be measured from the charge flowing in a closed electrical circuit when the specimen is inserted in or removed from it. The difference here is that the induction includes in it the contribution of induction which would be produced by the applied field itself if the specimen were absent. While the magnetization is used more in fundamental measurements of ferromagnetic properties, the induction is used technically. The relationship between the quantities differs according to the unit convention used and there is an unfortunate dichotomy between users. The unit systems are described in Section 1.2. The various quantities will now be used according to how they are defined in Section 1.2.

Starting with the unmagnetized piece of iron at room temperature we find that when a small increasing field is applied its magnetization increases at first slowly and reversibly. Beyond a critical field hysteresis develops. The magnetization does not return to zero when the field is switched off and if the field is cycled between small limits a minor hysteresis loop is followed. Eventually the magnetization rises more sharply with increasing field and at still higher fields saturation of the magnetization sets in. The hysteresis loop from saturation is a characteristic of the specimen and it is illustrated in Fig. 1.1a. The

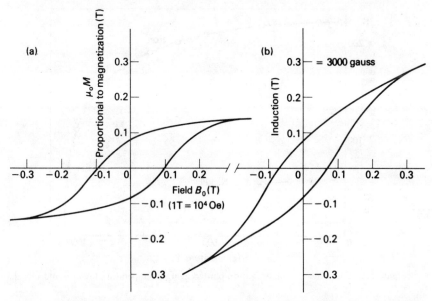

**Figure 1.1**    Magnetization (a) and induction (b) hysteresis loops of a hard magnetic material. The unit of the ordinate in (a) is $\mu_0 M$, equal to the magnetic polarization $J$.

remanence is thereby defined, which is the magnetization remaining when the field is switched off from saturation; and the coercivity is also defined, which is the reverse field required to reduce the magnetization to zero from saturation. The induction hysteresis loop has a different shape (Fig. 1.1b) and the induction coercivity has a different value. The hysteresis properties of ferromagnets are largely properties of arrangements of magnetic domains, and these are described in Chapter 6.

After saturation has been reached the magnetization increases very slowly and approximately linearly with increasing field. This is the intrinsic magnetization, which is the value of the magnetization within a domain. It is what remains when the different orientations of all the domains present have been allowed for. It is reached in strong fields because of the effect of increasing field on the domain orientation. The intrinsic magnetization of a ferromagnet does not become zero when the applied field is zero but it remains at a value only a little below its value in a strong field. This is the spontaneous magnetization, that which is spontaneously present within the domains when no field is applied externally. In iron at room temperature the difference between the spontaneous magnetization and the intrinsic magnetization measured in a strong field of about 5 T (50 kOe) is only detectable with difficulty.

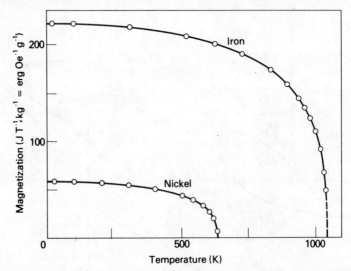

**Figure 1.2**  Spontaneous magnetization plotted against temperature for iron and nickel.

The spontaneous magnetization depends on temperature (Fig. 1.2), having its largest value at the absolute zero. It falls at an increasing rate with increasing temperature and becomes zero at a characteristic temperature $T_C$ called the Curie temperature. As the temperature rises the intrinsic magnetization varies increasingly with field (Fig. 1.3) and it becomes non-linearly dependent on the field as the Curie temperature is approached. This causes certain difficulties in measuring the spontaneous magnetization when $T$ approaches $T_C$, with consequent difficulties in the exact experimental definition of $T_C$ from magnetization measurements. The

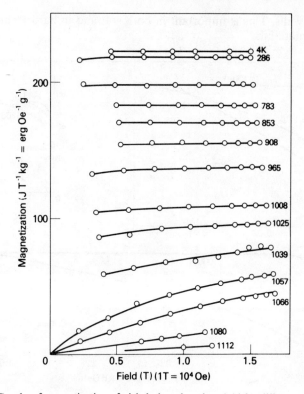

**Figure 1.3**  Graphs of magnetization of nickel plotted against field for different temperatures.

maximum value of the spontaneous magnetization (at $T = 0$) is directly related to the average magnetic moment per atom of the ferromagnet and it gives a measure of the number of magnetic carriers per atom.

If the magnetization of a single crystal of a ferromagnet is measured in a field increasing from zero it is found that the approach to saturation differs according to the orientation of the field with respect to the crystal axes. Some directions are directions of easy magnetization and others are hard directions. In iron (Fig. 1.4) the cube edge direction (100) is easy while the direction of the cube diagonal (111) is hard. This is a fundamental effect called magnetocrystalline anisotropy. The directionality of the magnetic moments of individual atoms interacts with the symmetry of their crystalline environment. Measurements on the effect lead to basic information on the nature of the magnetic atoms. The effect is very important in technical magnetism. Magnetocrystalline energy plays a large part in determining the thickness, energy and mobility of domain boundary walls. This is important in both soft and in hard technical magnetic materials.

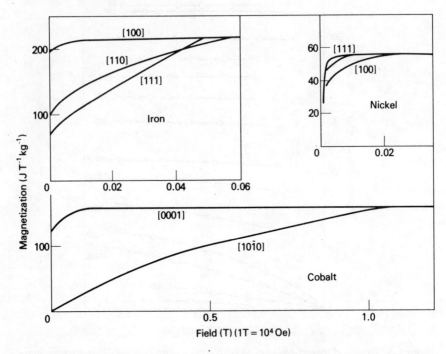

**Figure 1.4**  Magnetization as a function of field in single crystals of iron, nickel and cobalt, for different crystallographic directions.

Another effect observed in ferromagnets is the occurrence of small dimensional changes. The state of strain alters as the direction of the spontaneous magnetization rotates with respect to the crystal axes. This is magnetostriction. There is also a small volume magnetostriction as the spontaneous magnetization is altered by changing the temperature. Magnetostriction is fundamental and is due to the link between atomic magnetic moments and the crystalline lattice. It is important in technical magnetism, affecting the pinning of domain wall boundaries to crystalline imperfections.

The specific heat capacity of ferromagnetic materials contains a significant magnetic component $C_m$ superimposed on that part of the total specific heat capacity (mostly from the lattice and from the conduction electron gas) which would be present if the material were non-magnetic.

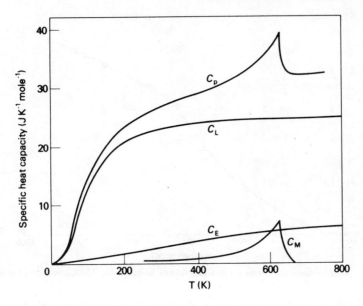

**Figure 1.5**   Specific heat capacity of nickel, as a function of temperature. The magnetic ($C_M$), lattice ($C_L$) and electronic contributions ($C_E$) to the total ($C_p$) are shown.

The sharp cusp in the graph of heat capacity against temperature (Fig. 1.5) at the Curie temperature is typical of a second-order thermodynamic phase change. It is associated with the disappearance of long-range magnetic order at $T_C$. The small magnetic heat capacity remaining just above $T_C$ arises from the presence of residual short-range magnetic order, the amount of which diminishes rapidly with increasing temperature. The entropy $\Delta S_m$ of the magnetic state may be obtained from measurements of the heat capacity. It is given by

$$\Delta S_m = \int \frac{C_m}{T} dT$$

evaluated over the whole range of temperature of the ferromagnetic state. The entropy of the magnetic state is related to the spin quantum number $S$ (and hence the magnetic moment) of the magnetic atoms by

$$\Delta S_m = cR \ln(2S+1)$$

where $c$ is the fraction of the atoms present carrying the magnetic moment and $R$ is the gas constant.

There is also a link between the magnetic state of a ferromagnet and its

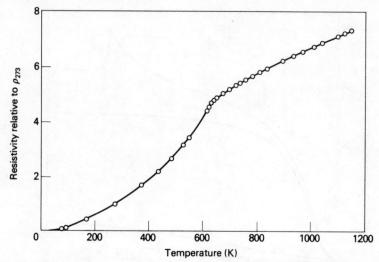

**Figure 1.6**   Relative resistance of nickel as a function of temperature. The Curie temperature is 631 K.

electrical resistivity. The dependence of the resistivity is illustrated in Fig. 1.6. Details of the relationship between magnetic order and resistivity are discussed in the book by Dugdale in this series. Since disorder of any kind contributes to resistivity we may expect the onset of magnetic order when a ferromagnetic specimen is cooled through its Curie temperature to be accompanied by a fall in resistivity.

### 1.1.2   *Paramagnetism*

Many solids are paramagnetic. When a field is applied to them they become magnetized, usually much more weakly than a ferromagnetic material. The magnetization depends linearly on the field and it always disappears when the field is removed (Fig. 1.7). The rate of change of magnetization with field is called the paramagnetic susceptibility, referred to unit mass of the specimen ($\chi$), to one mole ($\chi_m$) or to unit volume ($\kappa$).

Above their Curie temperature ferromagnets become paramagnetic and their susceptibility depends on temperature. The reciprocal of the susceptibility varies linearly with temperature, or nearly so (Fig. 1.8), with an intercept on the positive temperature axis at the paramagnetic Curie temperature $\theta_p$. $\theta_p$ is usually of the same order as $T_C$ but the two quantities are rarely exactly equal. This dependence of susceptibility on temperature of the form

$$\chi = C/(T - \theta_p)$$

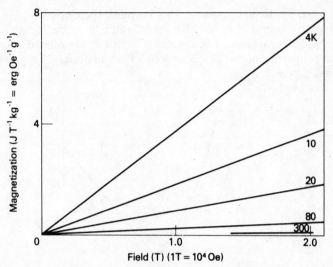

**Figure 1.7** Magnetizatiôn of hydrated copper sulphate as a function of field at different temperatures.

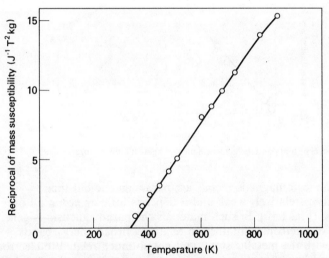

**Figure 1.8** Reciprocal susceptibility plotted against temperature for nickel–32% copper alloy, illustrating the Curie–Weiss law. $\theta_p$ is 336 K.

is known as the Curie–Weiss law.

Some other materials of which ordinary hydrated copper sulphate, $Cu\,SO_4 \cdot 5H_2O$, is an example (Fig. 1.9), follow a similar law at all ordinary temperatures but for them $\theta_p$ is zero. This becomes the Curie law, $\chi = C/T$. Negative values of $\theta_p$ are also found, often in antiferromagnetics above their Néel temperature. The constants $C$ and $\theta_p$ are related to fundamental properties of the atoms or ions of the materials. They are discussed in Chapter 2.

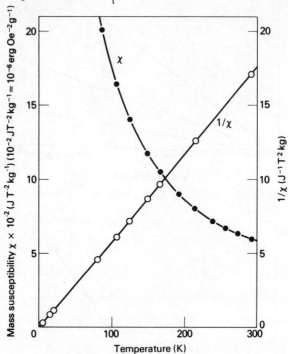

**Figure 1.9** Susceptibility and its reciprocal plotted against temperature for $CuSO_4.5H_2O$ (Curie law).

Many non-ferromagnetic metals are paramagnetic but their susceptibility is relatively weak and it depends little or not at all on temperature (Fig. 1.10). In such materials the paramagnetism is generally a property of electrons contained in relatively broad energy bands associated with the metallic state; and not so much related to electrons tightly bound into the ion cores of the atoms making up the metal. The properties of materials of this kind are discussed in Chapter 3.

### 1.1.3 *Diamagnetism*

Diamagnetic substances have a negative magnetic susceptibility. All

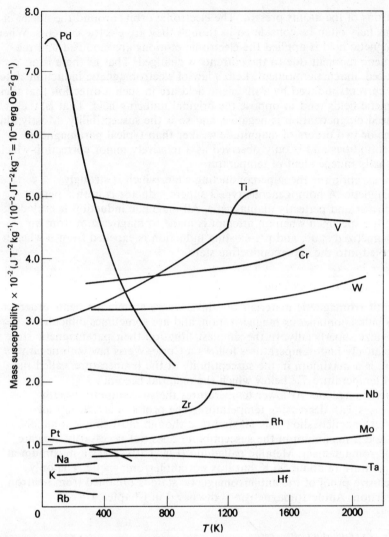

**Figure 1.10** Temperature dependence of the magnetic susceptibility of several metals. (After Kittel, *Introduction to Solid State Physics*, Wiley, London and New York.).

substances have a basic diamagnetic term but it is nearly always weak and it is very often masked by a much larger (positive) paramagnetic susceptibility. The basic diamagnetism is independent of temperature and is due to the effect of applied magnetic fields on the motion of inner electrons of the atoms present. The electronic orbits around the nuclei of atoms may often be considered as though they are electric currents. When a magnetic field is applied the electronic motions are modified and the magnetic moment due to the currents is changed. That is, there is an 'induced' magnetic moment. Lenz's law of electromagnetic induction states that currents induced by a magnetic field are in such a direction that their magnetic fields tend to oppose the original inducing field. That is, the induced magnetization is negative, and so is the susceptibility. Mostly, this is one or two orders of magnitude weaker than typical paramagnetic susceptibilities and is only observed as a relatively minor correction which is usually independent of temperature.

An exception is the superconducting state, which is strongly diamagnetic. A homogeneous type I superconductor is both a perfect conductor and perfectly diamagnetic. All magnetic induction is excluded from the specimen when an attempt is made to magnetize it from an unmagnetized state, and pre-existing induction is expelled from it when it is cooled into the superconducting state.

### 1.1.4   Antiferromagnetism

Antiferromagnetic materials are those where atomic moments order with zero bulk spontaneous magnetization, and are sometimes difficult to recognize superficially. In the simplest situation their paramagnetic state at relatively high temperatures follows a Curie–Weiss law with negative $\theta_p$. There is a maximum in the susceptibility at the temperature, called the Néel temperature $T_N$, below which the material becomes antiferromagnetic. At lower temperatures the susceptibility usually decreases with decreasing temperature. The problem is that not all antiferromagnets show this maximum, although most simple ionic ones do. And a maximum in the susceptibility does not necessarily indicate antiferromagnetism. Metallic palladium (Fig. 1.10) shows a maximum at a temperature of about 90 K but it is not antiferromagnetic. The only conclusive proof of the antiferromagnetic state is obtained from neutron diffraction. Antiferromagnetism is discussed in Chapter 4.

### 1.1.5   Ferrimagnetism

Ferrimagnetic materials are superficially similar to ferromagnets. They exhibit a spontaneous magnetic moment at temperature below their Curie temperature $T_C$. Hysteresis and domain properties are observed in a similar way and they become paramagnetic at temperatures above $T_C$. One difference is that ferromagnets are usually metallic and ferrimagnets are usually non-metals. But this is not an exclusive separation and it is not

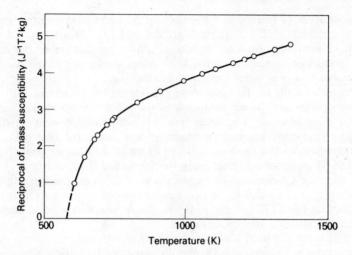

**Figure 1.11** Reciprocal susceptibility plotted against temperature for a specimen of ferrimagnetic manganese ferrite $MnO.Fe_2O_3$.

one based on the fundamental magnetism.

A more reliable difference that is observed experimentally is that the susceptibility of most ferromagnets measured above $T_C$ follows the Curie–Weiss law reasonably well (at any rate within a few parts per hundred), but the susceptibility of most ferrimagnets does not follow this law until relatively high temperatures are reached. The graph of $1/\chi$ against $T$ is often hyperbolic at temperatures up to about $2\ T_C$, becoming linear asymptotically (Fig. 1.11). At temperatures below $T_C$ the temperature dependence of the spontaneous magnetization is often recognizably different from that for ferromagnets. A great variety of shapes of graphs of spontaneous magnetization against temperature is found experimentally (see Fig. 4.12). Magnetic neutron diffraction gives a certain confirmation of a ferrimagnetic state. Many ferrimagnetic materials have very important technical applications. Ferrimagnetic properties are described in Chapter 4.

## 1.2 Units in magnetism

It is important at this stage to consider the definition of units of the quantities that are commonly used in magnetism. The chief reason for this is to draw attention to the diversity of unit systems currently in use, and to try to provide a simple guide to conversion between the different systems.

In most areas of science and engineering, SI units have by now been adopted completely. The base units are the metre, kilogram, second, ampere, kelvin (temperature), candela (luminous intensity) and the mole. There are numerous derived units. The system works well in many applications and it is widely accepted in teaching.

When polarizable media have to be considered the system is not uniquely defined and its advantages over the older 'unrationalized' CGS system are not obvious. The latter system is self-consistent and satisfactory and there has been a marked reluctance of workers in the field of ferromagnetism to change from CGS to SI units. Textbooks tend to be written in SI units and original work in magnetism is mostly in electromagnetic CGS units. The application of SI to magnetism can be contradictory and confusing. A vast amount of older information is firmly established in the CGS system. Many research papers published currently in different countries are in CGS units.

Since SI units are used almost everywhere else the case is strong that those working in ferromagnetism should make the transition. Great care is still needed in the establishment of preferred SI units in magnetism so that conversion between the two systems shall be simple, straightforward and unambiguous. Translation factors involving multiples of $4\pi$ are to be avoided if at all possible. In this connection the SI definition of magnetic susceptibility needs special care.

The main differences of principle between the CGS and the SI systems applied to magnetism are:

(i) In the SI system formulae dealing with force, energy, magnetic moment and so on are in terms of the induction $B$. The magnetic force $H$ is rarely used alone. It only arises in calculating the magnetic effect of an electric current, or in similar cases. Whenever $H$ interacts with any other quantity the permeability of free space $\mu_0$ must be introduced. In free space $B_0 = \mu_0 H$. The value of $\mu_0$ is $4\pi \times 10^{-7}$ H m$^{-1}$.

In the CGS system the formulae are in terms of the field strength $H$ measured in oersteds. The permeability of free space is unity so that the induction (measured in gauss) in free space is numerically equal to the field.

In applying SI to magnetism there has seemed hitherto to be an arbitrary choice available between two alternatives. The Kennelly system (1936) was accepted first by electrical engineers. Physicists have been less ready to adopt it and various bodies have expressed a preference for the version proposed by Sommerfeld (1948). However, these two systems need not be contradictory or mutually exclusive.

(ii) The induction $B$ in a polarizable medium is given in the SI system by $B = \mu_0(H + M) = B_0 + \mu_0 M$, where $M$ is the magnetization per unit volume. This is the Sommerfeld system. In the Kennelly system

$B = \mu_0 H + J$, where $J$ is the magnetic polarization. There seems to be no reason whatever why the Sommerfeld and Kennelly systems should not both be employed, so long as there is a distinctive nomenclature. Whichever is the more convenient for a given situation may be used.

In the CGS system induction in the medium is given by $B = H + 4\pi I$, where $I$ is the magnetization per unit volume and is analogous to $M$.

The need to distinguish between the two kinds of induction, that which would be present in free space if the medium were absent and that actually present in the medium, has been a stumbling block in applying the SI system to magnetism. In this book the 'free space induction' ($= \mu_0 H$) is given the symbol $B_0$ and called the field in SI. It is measured in teslas (T). $H$ is measured in SI units of ampere metre$^{-1}$. It is currently used by some electrical engineers but it is not very useful where comparisons have to be made with fields measured in CGS units. $B_0$ can be used synonymously with the field $H$ in CGS, so long as it is remembered that $B_0$ is really a free space induction. The 'induction in a medium' is called the induction $B$ in both systems.

Continuity at boundaries needs to be specified clearly. In CGS the normal component of the induction $B$ and the tangential component of the field $H$ are continuous across the boundary between different media. In SI there is no difference in principle. The normal component of the induction $B$ and the tangential component of the field $B_0 = \mu_0 H$ remain continuous at the boundary.

In many cases it is more satisfactory to standardize measurements against unit mass than against unit volume, since it is easier to measure mass accurately. The magnetization per unit mass $\sigma$ is given by $\sigma = M/\rho$ (SI), where $\rho$ is the density, or by $\sigma = I/\rho$ (CGS).

It is the definition of susceptibility in SI which causes most confusion. Different authors define susceptibility differently. In the Sommerfeld system the volume susceptibility is the magnetization divided by the field. In the Kennelly system it is the polarization divided by the field. But the question arises of how to define the field.

In this book we define the volume susceptibility in SI (Sommerfeld) as the ratio between the magnetization and the field $B_0$ which produces it.

$$\kappa = M/B_0 = M/(\mu_0 H)$$

This is to be preferred because it converts easily with the CGS system.

The question of the torque acting on a dipole in a field also needs different handling in the Sommerfeld and Kennelly schemes, because of the different definitions of dipole moment. The Sommerfeld magnetization dipole moment is $m_S = VM$, where $V$ is the volume of the specimen. The torque is $T = m_S \times (\mu_0 H) = m_S \times B_0 = VM \times B_0$. The Kennelly

**Table 1.1**   Units in magnetism.

| Quantity | SI | CGS (emu) |
|---|---|---|
| Permeability of free space | $\mu_0 = 4\pi \times 10^{-7} H\,m^{-1}$ | *unity* |
| Induction in free space (field) | $B_0$ tesla (T) | $B$ gauss (G) |
| | $1\,T = 10^4\,G$ | |
| Magnetic force (field) | $H$ $A\,m^{-1}$ | $H$ oersted (Oe) |
| | $1\,A\,m^{-1} = 1\cdot257 \times 10^{-2}\,Oe$ | |
| | $79\cdot58\,A\,m^{-1} = 1\,Oe$ | |
| Induction in free space (field) | $B_0 = \mu_0 H$ | $B = H$ |
| | 1 T equivalent to $10^4$ Oe | |
| Induction in medium | $B = B_0 + M\mu_0$ | $B = H + 4\pi I$ |
| | $1\,T = 10^4\,g$ | |
| Magnetization per unit volume | $M$   $J\,T^{-1}\,m^{-3}$ or $A\,m^{-1}$ | $I$ erg $Oe^{-1}\,cm^{-1}$ |
| | $1\,J\,T^{-1}\,m^{-3} = 10^{-3}$ erg $Oe^{-1}\,cm^{-3}$ | |
| | $10^3\,J\,T^{-1}\,m^{-3} = 1$ erg $Oe^{-1}\,cm^{-3}$ | |
| Magnetization per unit mass | $\sigma = M/\rho\,J\,T^{-1}\,kg^{-1}$ | $\sigma = I/\rho$ erg $Oe^{-1}\,g^{-1}$ |
| | $\rho = $ density | |
| | $1\,J\,T^{-1}\,kg^{-1} = 1$ erg $Oe^{-1}\,g^{-1}$ | |
| Magnetic polarization defined by | $J$ (T) | $4\pi I$ (G) |
| | $B = B_0 + J$ | $B = H + 4\pi I$ |
| Sommerfeld magnetization dipole moment | $m_S = VM$ | |
| | $V = $ volume | |
| Kennelly polarization dipole moment | $m_K = VJ$ | |
| Susceptibility per unit volume | $\kappa = M/B_0\,J\,T^{-2}\,m^{-3}$ | $\kappa = I/H$ erg $Oe^{-2}\,cm^{-3}$ |
| | $10\,J\,T^{-2}\,m^{-3} = 10^{-6}$ erg $Oe^{-2}\,cm^{-3}$ | |
| Susceptibility per unit mass | $\chi = \kappa/\rho\,J\,T^{-2}\,kg^{-1}$ | $\chi = \kappa/\rho$ erg $Oe^{-2}\,g^{-1}$ |
| | $10^{-2}\,J\,T^{-2}\,kg^{-1} = 10^{-6}$ erg $Oe^{-2}\,g^{-1}$ | |
| Susceptibility per mole $\chi_M$ | $10^{-5}\,J\,T^{-2}$ $mole^{-1} = 10^{-6}$ erg $Oe^{-2}\,mole^{-1}$ | |
| Force on ferromagnetic specimen in field gradient | $F_z = m\,\sigma\,dB_0/dz$ | $F_z = m\,\sigma\,dH/dz$ |
| Force on paramagnetic specimen | $F_z = m\,\chi\,B_0\,dB_0/dz$ | $F_z = m\,\chi\,H\,dH/dz$ |
| Bohr magneton | $\mu_B = eh/4\pi m$ | $\mu_B = eh/4\pi mc$ |
| | $= 9\cdot2732 \times 10^{-24}\,J\,T^{-1}$ | $= 9\cdot2732 \times 10^{-21}$ erg $Oe^{-1}$ |
| Relative permeability | $\mu = B/B_0 = 1 + \mu_0\kappa$ | $\mu = B/H = 1 + 4\pi\kappa$ |
| | same value in both systems | |
| Torque | $T = VM \times B_0$ (Sommerfeld) | $T = VI \times H$ |
| | $T = VJ \times H$ (Kennelly) | |
| | $V = $ volume | |
| Demagnetizing field | $(B_0)_D = DM$   $D = \mu_0 N/4\pi$ | $(H)_D = NI$ |

polarization dipole moment is $m_K = VJ$. The torque is $T = m_K \times H$
$= VJ \times H = V\mu_0 M \times B_0/\mu_0$, since $J = \mu_0 M$ and $B_0 = \mu_0 H$. These results
are clearly the same. The Sommerfeld scheme is usually more convenient
for the physicist since $H$ need never enter. The Bohr magneton is defined
in this book as a Sommerfeld magnetization dipole moment. How it arises
is discussed in Section 2.1.

The more common conversions of units between SI and CGS are given
in Table 1.1.

# 2

# Localized Magnetism Associated with the Ion Cores

## 2.1 The origins of the magnetic properties of materials

Magnetism can be seen in a simple model as originating in the motion of electric charges; that is, moving electrons. The quantized nature of the motion of the electrons gives rise to a fundamental unit of magnetic dipole moment, the Bohr magneton $\mu_B$. How it arises can be seen as follows.

The dipole moment associated with a loop of electric current $I$ is $IA$, where $A$ is the area of the loop. If the current consists of an electron of charge $e$ and mass $m$ rotating in a circular orbit of radius $r$ at angular velocity $\omega$, the magnetic dipole moment

$$\mu = IA = -\tfrac{1}{2}er \times v = -e(\omega/2\pi)\pi r^2 = -\tfrac{1}{2}e\omega r^2$$

The angular momentum

$$J = mr \times v = m\omega r^2$$

That is,

$$\mu = -(e/2m)J$$

The angular momentum is quantized in units of $h/2\pi$, where $h$ is Planck's constant. Thus the lowest non-zero value for $\mu$ is

$$\mu_B = eh/4\pi m$$

Its value is $9 \cdot 2732 \times 10^{-24}$ J T$^{-1}$ (SI), or $9 \cdot 2732 \times 10^{-21}$ erg Oe$^{-1}$ (CGS).

This treatment is for the special case of a simple electron orbit. More generally (and including the case of electron spin) $\mu = \gamma J$, where $\gamma$ is called the magnetomechanical ratio. For pure orbital motion of an electron $\gamma = -e/2m$. For pure electron spin $\gamma = -e/m$.

## 2.2 The magnetic moment of a single atom

The magnetic properties of solid materials are determined fundamentally by the characteristics of the individual atoms present, and

by the electrons associated with these atoms. In trying to understand the properties that are observed experimentally, we are concerned with the ways in which all the atoms and electrons in the solid interact in order to give the whole effect. A fuller description of atomic structures is given in the book in the present series by Coles and Caplin.

Four quantum numbers, $n$, $l$, $m_l$ and $s$ are required to describe the state of an electron in an atom. A given electron shell, defined by electrons all having the same principal quantum number $n$, is full when it contains $2n^2$ electrons. Transitions between different $n$ levels do not concern us in considering the magnetic properties of solids, because the energy differences involved (measured from atomic spectra) are of the order of $10^6$ cm$^{-1}$. $l$ can take the values 0, 1, 2, ... $(n-1)$. The magnetic quantum number $m_l$ has $(2l+1)$ possible values; $-l$, $(-l+1)$, ... 0, ... $(l-1)$, $l$. The spin quantum number $s$ is $\frac{1}{2}$ and $m_s = \pm\frac{1}{2}$. Thus for any allowed value of $l$ there are $2(2l+1)$ levels. $l$ values are usually indicated by the spectroscopic notation

symbol s p d f g h ...
$l$     0 1 2 3 4 5 ...

Much of the discussion in magnetism is to do with transition elements and d-electrons ($l = 2$); or with rare earths and f-electrons ($l = 3$).

How the electrons combine in an atom to produce a stable state of least energy (the ground state) is determined partly by the relative magnitudes of the energies of interaction of the following types. The vectors $l_{i,k}$ and $s_{i,k}$ represent respectively the orbital and the spin angular momenta of the $i$th and the $k$th electrons in the atom.

$a_{ik}\, l_i.s_k$; this is the spin–orbit interaction, either for the interaction between the orbital angular momentum of one electron and its own spin ($i = k$) or for the same interaction between different electrons.

$b_{ik}\, l_i.l_k$; this is the orbit–orbit interaction between different electrons.

$c_{ik}\, s_i.s_k$; this is the spin–spin interaction between different electrons.

For the spin–orbit interaction, the orbital angular momentum of a given electron interacts more strongly with its own than with other spins, and $|a_{ii}| \gg |a_{ik}|$. The dominant mechanism in determining $a_{ii}$ is the electrostatic coupling between $l_i$ and $s_i$ through the interaction of both with the nuclear charge. $a_{ii}$ is largest for heavy atoms with high atomic number.

If the constants $a$, $b$ and $c$ are all of the same order of magnitude, the problem of the energy and nature of the atomic motion becomes complex. It is found experimentally that in most cases, except for the heaviest elements, the spin–orbit constants $a_{ii}$ and $a_{ik}$ are small compared with $b_{ik}$ and $c_{ik}$. The spins form a resultant vector $S$ for the whole atom and the orbital momenta form a resultant $L$. The corresponding atomic quantum numbers are $S$ and $L$ The spin–orbit interaction can then be regarded as a

relatively small (but not usually zero) coupling between $L$ and $S$. When external influences are not too strong, $S$ and $L$ are combined into a resultant vector $J$. The corresponding quantum number $J$ can take the values

$$J = |L-S|, |L-S+1|, \ldots |L+S-1|, |L+S|$$

It should be remembered that while we deal here with these vectors in a simple geometrical way, in a fuller quantum mechanical treatment they are matrices (see Coles and Caplin, 1976, *The Electronic Structures of Solids*, Arnold, London).

The projection $M_J$ of $J$ in the direction of quantization is also quantized and

$$M_J = -J, -J+1, \ldots J-1, J$$

In a given atom the maximum values of $L$ and $S$ are given by $\Sigma l_i$ and $\Sigma s_i$ respectively but other values can occur between the limits of $\Sigma \pm l_i$ and $\Sigma \pm s_i$ given by $\Sigma m_l$ and $\Sigma m_s$. The choice of $L$ and $S$ is made by applying Hund's rules. These are essentially empirical, and first arose in interpreting atomic spectra.

*Hund's rules*

(1) The combination of $s_i$ that gives the lowest energy (most stable) is that with the highest value of $(2S+1)$.

(2) If when the first rule was been satisfied there are several possible $L$ values all having the same value of $(2S+1)$, that with the largest $L$ will be the most stable.

Hund's rules have full theoretical justification only in very limited cases; but there is little doubt of their validity, at any rate for the lighter elements. The physical argument to support them is as follows.

(i) Dual occupation of a spatial electron distribution (two electrons of opposite spin in one 'orbital') must involve large electrostatic electron–electron repulsions because of the proximity of the two electrons. Energy is lowered if dual occupations are minimized, giving as many like spins as possible. The operation of this rule leads directly to the possession of relatively large magnetic moments by partially filled d- and f-electron shells, in transition elements and rare earths.

(ii) Having satisfied the first condition, if the electrons orbit in the same sense ($l_i$ has the same sign) electron–electron repulsive interactions are minimized because the electrons spend more of the time further apart. Under this condition $L$ takes the largest value compatible with the configuration and the first condition.

The energies associated with rule 1 are of a larger order of magnitude than those associated with the second rule.

The following examples illustrate the application of the rules.

(a) $Co^{2+}$ ion, in a $3d^7$-state. For 3d-electrons $l_i = 2$

$$
\begin{array}{llllllll|lll}
m_s & \tfrac{1}{2} & \tfrac{1}{2} & \tfrac{1}{2} & \tfrac{1}{2} & \tfrac{1}{2} & -\tfrac{1}{2} & -\tfrac{1}{2} & -\tfrac{1}{2} & \tfrac{1}{2} & -\tfrac{1}{2} \\
m_l & 2 & 1 & 0 & -1 & -2 & 2 & 1 & 0 & -1 & -2
\end{array}
$$

Counting the seven electrons from the left we have

$$S = \tfrac{3}{2};\ 2S+1 = 4;\ L = 3$$

(b) $Dy^{3+}$ ion, in a $4f^9$-state. For 4f-electrons $l_i = 3$

$$
\begin{array}{lllllllll|llllll}
m_s & \tfrac{1}{2} & \tfrac{1}{2} & \tfrac{1}{2} & \tfrac{1}{2} & \tfrac{1}{2} & \tfrac{1}{2} & \tfrac{1}{2} & -\tfrac{1}{2} & -\tfrac{1}{2} & -\tfrac{1}{2} & -\tfrac{1}{2} & -\tfrac{1}{2} & -\tfrac{1}{2} & -\tfrac{1}{2} \\
m_l & 3 & 2 & 1 & 0 & -1 & -2 & -3 & 3 & 2 & 1 & 0 & -1 & -2 & -3
\end{array}
$$

Counting the nine electrons from the left we have

$$S = \tfrac{5}{2};\ 2S+1 = 6;\ L = 5.$$

## Combination of L and S to form J

If there were no spin–orbit interaction all the $(2S+1)$ (when $L$ exceeds $S$) or $(2L+1)$ (when $S$ exceeds $L$) possible values of $J$ would correspond to the same energy. We now consider how the multiplets are split by spin–orbit interaction.

By analogy with the previous case the atomic spin–orbit coupling energy is written as

$$W_J = A\ L.S$$

The constant $A$ is related to some combination of the individual constants $a_{ik}$ and it is expected to be dominated by the interaction of spins with their own orbital momenta. We may regard it as a quantity known from experiment. It is positive when the electron shell is less than half full and negative when it is more than half full. If we write

$$J^2 = (L+S)^2 = L^2 + S^2 + 2L.S$$

then

$$W_J = \tfrac{1}{2}A\,(J^2 - L^2 - S^2)$$

When $A$ is positive, $W_J$ is least when $J$ (and therefore $J$) is least. $J = |L-S|$ gives the lowest energy and $J = |L+S|$ gives the highest, and *vice versa* when $A$ is negative. When an electron shell is less than half full the most stable multiplet component is $J = |L-S|$. When it is more than half full the multiplets are inverted and the most stable component is $J = |L+S|$. At the half-way point $L = 0$ and $J = S$. When the shell is filled completely $L$, $S$ and $J$ are all zero and the shell is magnetically inactive, except for a weak diamagnetic contribution. The range of energy between the lowest and highest multiplets is $|\frac{1}{2}A[J(J+1)_{max} - J(J+1)_{min}]|$. For $Co^{2+}$ $A$ is $-180$ cm$^{-1}$ and the energy range is 1890 cm$^{-1}$.

Each multiplet state ($J$) contains $(2J+1)$ sub-states, levels, corresponding to the different allowed values of $M_J$. In the free atom, when no external fields are applied, all the levels of a given state will have the same energy. Applying a magnetic field separates the energies of the levels and removes the degeneracy†. Most of the fundamental magnetic properties of materials stem from changes in the total energy as atoms are redistributed among these levels when magnetic fields are applied, or when the temperature is changed. A state for which $J = 0$ (or $2J+1 = 1$) cannot produce a magnetic moment, because no change in distribution (or energy) can take place under the influence of a field. Fig. 2.1 illustrates the scheme of energy levels for the $Co^{2+}$ ion in the free state.

The quantum numbers of a multiplet state are often written in spectroscopic notation in the form $^{2S+1}L_J$, or for a sub-level of this state $^{2S+1}L_J{}^{M_J}$ using the code for $L$

| symbol | S | P | D | F | G | H | ... |
|--------|---|---|---|---|---|---|-----|
| $L$ | 0 | 1 | 2 | 3 | 4 | 5 | ... |

Thus the two examples given previously, $Co^{2+}$ and $Dy^{3+}$, are respectively in the states $^4F_{9/2}$ (for which there are ten $M_J$ sub-levels) and $^6H_{15/2}$ (sixteen sub-levels).

### 2.2.1  Units of magnetic moment

In connecting the quantum numbers $L$, $S$ and $J$ with the angular momentum vectors $L$, $S$ and $J$ we write, for the general case

$$L^2 = L(L+1)(h/2\pi)^2$$
$$S^2 = S(S+1)(h/2\pi)^2$$
$$J^2 = J(J+1)(h/2\pi)^2$$

The reason for this particular form is connected with the fact that we deal with the sum of three Cartesian components of the angular momenta and these angular momenta are really matrices. In contrast, the projection of the total angular momentum $J$ in the direction of a single axis of quantization (such as the direction of an applied magnetic field) is given by $M_J(h/2\pi)$.

† Crystal fields in solids can also lift this degeneracy in a more complicated way: see Section 2.4.3.

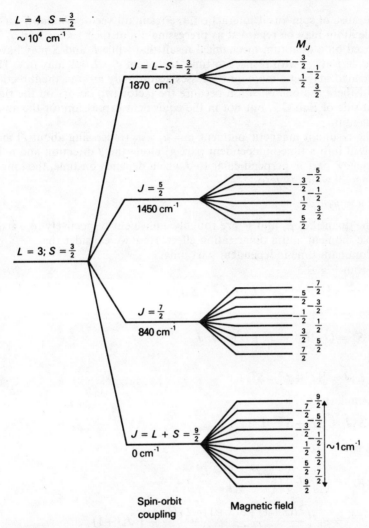

**Figure 2.1**   Energy levels of the Co ion in the free state (not drawn to scale).

The corresponding magnetic moment vectors are

$$\mu_L = \mu_B \left[L(L+1)\right]^{\frac{1}{2}} \tag{2.1}$$

$$\mu_S = 2\mu_B \left[S(S+1)\right]^{\frac{1}{2}} \tag{2.2}$$

and $\mu_J$, where $\mu_B$ is the Bohr magneton.

Because of spin–orbit interaction, the resultant vectors $L$ and $S$ for the whole atom may be regarded as precessing about their vector sum $J$. This is based on a quantum mechanical result that while $L$ and $S$ may have finite derivatives with respect to time, their sum $J = L + S$ may not. The associated magnetic moment precesses accordingly around the direction of $J$, but there is a complication because the factor two occurs on the right-hand side of Equ. 2.2, but not in the equivalent expression for the angular momentum.

The resultant magnetic moment $\mu = \mu_L + \mu_S$ (precessing about $J$) may be resolved into a time-independent part $\mu_J$ along the $J$ direction and a 'high-frequency' part $\mu'$ perpendicular to $J$ which depends on time, the long-time average of which is zero:

$$\mu = \mu_J + \mu'$$

The quantities $\mu_J$ and $\mu'$ are roughly equivalent respectively to a fixed dipole moment and a polarization effect. Here we consider the predominant time-independent part only.

From Fig. 2.2

$$\mu_J{}^2 = [(2\pi/h)\mu_B]^2 \, (L.J/|J| + 2 \, S.J/|J|)^2$$

Since

$$S^2 = (J-L)^2 = J^2 + L^2 - 2L.J$$

then

$$L.J = \tfrac{1}{2}(J^2 + L^2 - S^2)$$

and similarly

$$S.J = \tfrac{1}{2}(J^2 + S^2 - L^2)$$

That is,

$$\mu_J{}^2 = \left(\frac{2\pi}{h}\mu_B\right)^2 \left(\frac{3J^2 + S^2 - L^2}{2|J|^2}\right)^2 J^2$$

$$= \mu_B{}^2 \left(\frac{3J(J+1) + S(S+1) - L(L+1)}{2J(J+1)}\right)^2 J(J+1) \tag{2.3}$$

or,

$$\mu_J = g\,\mu_B[J(J+1)]^{\frac{1}{2}} \tag{2.4}$$

where

$$g = 1 + \frac{J(J+1) + S(S+1) - L(L+1)}{2J(J+1)} \tag{2.5}$$

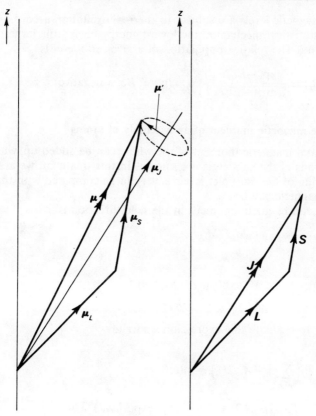

**Figure 2.2**   Vector atom model.

is the Landé $g$ factor and has the value 2 when $L = 0$ and the value 1
when $S = 0$.

This defines the magnetic moment of a single atom. In the absence of
an applied field all atoms having the same moment have the same energy.
When a magnetic field $B_0$ is applied, the energy depends on which of the
possible orientations, represented by the $(2J + 1)$ values of $M_J$, is taken up.

The magnetic energy of a given atom is

$$E_M = -\mu_J . B_0 = -g\,\mu_B M_J B_0$$

This is usually in the range 0·1 to 10 cm$^{-1}$, for applied fields of the order
of 1T ($10^4$ Oe). At room temperature the thermal energy $kT$ is about
200 cm$^{-1}$.

The magnetic levels are subject to thermal excitation according to the laws of statistical mechanics, the lowest energy having the largest population. The relative population of a given sub-level is

$$P(M_J) = \frac{\exp(-E_M/kT)}{\Sigma \exp(-E_M/kT)} \qquad \text{(note: } E_M \text{ is negative)}$$

## 2.3  The magnetic moment of an assembly of atoms

The total magnetic moment of the whole can be added up, when the populations of the sub-levels are known. In this treatment we assume that the spacing of the multiplet levels is very large compared with the splitting of the magnetic sub-levels.

The mean magnetic moment in the field direction is

$$\langle \mu_{J\uparrow} \rangle = \sum_{M_J} g\,\mu_B M_J P(M_J)$$

or

$$\frac{\langle \mu_{J\uparrow} \rangle}{g\,\mu_B} = \frac{\Sigma_{M_J} M_J \exp(g\,\mu_B M_J B_0/kT)}{\Sigma_{M_J} \exp(g\,\mu_B M_J B_0/kT)}$$

In order to evaluate this expression we write

$$u = \ln\!\left( \sum_{M_J} \exp(M_J y/J) \right) = \ln(v)$$

where $y = J\,g\,\mu_B B_0/kT$ and $v = \Sigma_{M_J} \exp(M_J y/J)$. Then

$$\frac{du}{dy} = \frac{du}{dv}\cdot\frac{dv}{dy} = \frac{\Sigma_{M_J} M_J/J \, \exp(M_J y/J)}{\Sigma_{M_J} \exp(M_J y/J)} = \frac{1}{J}\frac{\langle \mu_{J\uparrow} \rangle}{g\,\mu_B}$$

The problem is now to evaluate the sum

$$v = \sum_{M_J = -J}^{+J} \exp(M_J y/J)$$

This may be seen as the sum of a simple geometric progression as follows. Let $z = \exp(y/J)$, so that $\exp(M_J y/J) = z^{M_J}$. Then

$$v = \sum_{-J}^{+J} z^{M_J} = z^{-J}(1 + z + z^2 + \ldots z^{2J})$$

$$= \frac{z^{-J}(z^{2J+1}-1)}{z-1} = \frac{z^{(J+\frac{1}{2})}-z^{-(J+\frac{1}{2})}}{z^{\frac{1}{2}}-z^{-\frac{1}{2}}}$$

$$= \frac{\exp[(1+1/2J)y]-\exp[-(1+1/2J)y]}{\exp(y/2J)-\exp(-y/2J)} = \frac{\sinh(1+1/2J)y}{\sinh(y/2J)}$$

and

$$\frac{dv}{dy} = \frac{(1+1/2J)\sinh(y/2J)\cosh(1+1/2J)y-1/2J\sinh(1+1/2J)y\cosh(y/2J)}{[\sinh(y/2J)]^2}$$

Also,

$$du/dv = 1/v$$

Thus,

$$du/dy = (du/dv)(dv/dy) = \langle \mu_{J\uparrow} \rangle/J\, g\, \mu_B$$

$$= (1+1/2J)\coth[(1+1/2J)y]-1/2J\coth(y/2J)$$

$$= F(J,y) \qquad (2.6)$$

where $y = J\, g\, \mu_B B_0/kT$.

$F(J,y)$ is known as the Brillouin function. It is shown in Fig. 2.3 as a function of $y$, for selected values of $J$. In the special (but common) case when $J = \frac{1}{2}$

$$F(J, y) = 2\coth 2y - \coth y = \tanh y \qquad (2.6)$$

The other notable case is the classical one where there is a continuous range of orientations of $\mathbf{J}$. That is when $(2J+1) = \infty$, and $J = \infty$. This applies to the phenomenon of superparamagnetism, referred to later.

The saturation value (for large $y$) is where $F(J,y) = 1$, and all the atomic moments are aligned in the field direction. This condition is normally reached only in ferromagnets but it has been observed in strong fields and at low temperatures in some paramagnets, as shown in Fig. 2.4.

## 2.4 Paramagnetic susceptibility of an array of atoms

Observations are usually made on paramagnetic materials under the condition of small $y$; that is, near the origin of the Brillouin function. The paramagnetic susceptibility is related to the initial slope of the Brillouin curve.

When $x$ is small, $\coth x = 1/x + x/3 \,(-x^2/45)$. That is, for small $y$,

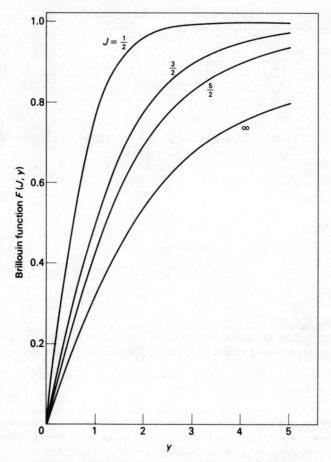

**Figure 2.3**  Brillouin function $F(J,y)$ for $J = \frac{1}{2}, \frac{3}{2}, \frac{5}{2}$ and $\infty$.

$$F(J,y) = 1/y + y/3 \; 1/2J \, (1 + 1/2J)^2 - 1/y - y/3 \, (1/2J)^2 = y(J+1)/3J$$

In one mole there are $N$ atoms. The total magnetic moment per mole is

$$N \langle \mu_{J\uparrow} \rangle = N J g \mu_B F(J,y) = N g^2 \mu_B^2 J(J+1) B_0 / 3kT$$

The susceptibility per mole

$$\chi_m = \text{moment}/B_0 = g^2 J(J+1) N \mu_B^2 / 3kT = p_{\text{eff}}^2 N \mu_B^2 / 3kT \qquad (2.7)$$

$p_{\text{eff}} = g[J(J+1)]^{\frac{1}{2}}$ is a useful quantity for comparing the properties of different materials, and it is easy to measure experimentally. It is called the effective paramagnetic Bohr magneton number, for historical reasons.

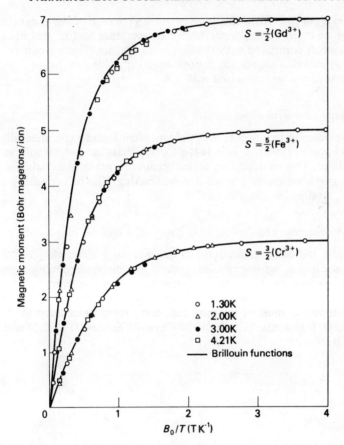

**Figure 2.4** Paramagnetic saturation in salts containing the ions $Gd^{3+}$, $Fe^{3+}$ and $Cr^{3+}$: The magnetic moment is plotted against the ratio of the field to the temperature. (After Henry, 1952, *Phys. Rev.*, **88**, 559.)

It is found by experiment that for many materials of the kind considered here the Curie law $\chi_m = C_m T^{-1}$ is obeyed, where $C_m$ is the molar Curie constant.

Thus

$$p_{eff}^2 = (3k/N\mu_B{}^2)C_m \simeq \begin{cases} 0 \cdot 8 \, C_m \, \text{(in SI units)} \\ 8 \, C_m \, \text{(in CGS units)} \end{cases}$$

A fuller treatment of the paramagnetism of free ions gives the result

$$\chi_m = p_{eff}^2 N \mu_B{}^2 / 3kT + \alpha_J$$

The term $\alpha_J$ derives from the 'high-frequency' part $\mu'$ of the magnetic moment of an atom. It is independent of temperature and in very many cases is so small compared with the first term that its effect cannot be observed. $\alpha_J$ makes a significant contribution only if the multiplet separation is not large compared with $kT$.

### 2.4.1  Comparison with experiment

The first point to mention is that the law often found experimentally is of the form $\chi = C(T - \theta)^{-1}$. This is the Curie–Weiss law, which will be discussed later. The modification arises because in many materials the atomic magnetic moments are not non-interacting. The relationship between $C_m$ and $p_{eff}$ is not affected.

### 2.4.2  Experimental behaviour of rare earth salts and metals

Many salts and other compounds of the rare earth elements are paramagnetic and at appropriate temperatures their susceptibility follows a Curie–Weiss law, $\chi = C(T - \theta)^{-1}$. Values of $p_{eff}$ derived from measurements on different salts of the same ion generally agree well. Also, the susceptibility of most of the pure rare earth metals measured at relatively high temperatures follows the Curie–Weiss law (Fig. 2.5) and the

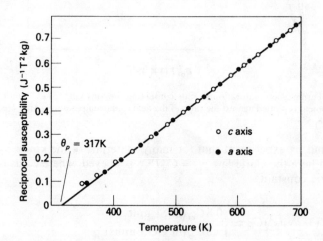

**Figure 2.5**   Reciprocal susceptibility of metallic gadolinium above the Curie temperature. (After Nigh, Legvold and Spedding, 1963, *Phys. Rev.*, **132**, 1092.)

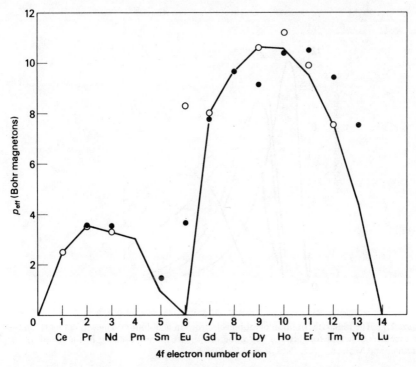

**Figure 2.6** Experimental and calculated values of $p_{eff}$ for rare earths. ○, metal; ●, sesquioxide $R_2O_3$; line, calculated.

respective values of $p_{eff}$ are similar to those of the salts. Experimental values of $p_{eff}$ are compared with those calculated from the simple theory in Fig. 2.6. In most cases the agreement is good.

The quality of this agreement indicates that the magnetic electrons in the rare earth atoms or ions are relatively little affected by external influences. The 4f-electrons, are deep in the atoms and are fairly well screened from intra-crystalline electric fields by a significant outer electron distribution which includes the 5s and 5p closed shells. The radial charge distributions of the various atomic electron levels calculated for $Gd^{3+}$ ions are shown in Fig. 2.7.

The most obvious discrepancies shown in Fig. 2.6 are for samarium and europium. The reason for the disagreements is that for these two elements the multiplet intervals cannot be regarded as infinitely large compared with $kT$. The multiplet spacings are shown in Fig. 2.8. When the intervals are comparable to $kT$ account must be taken of statistical occupation of higher multiplets and their magnetic sub-levels. The treatment is more

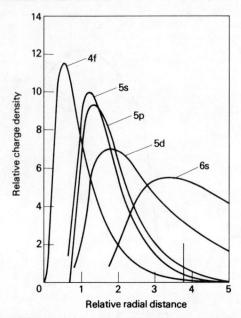

**Figure 2.7**  The radial distribution of atomic electrons in gadolinium. The vertical mark on the distance axis indicates roughly the half-value of the interatomic distance in the metal. (After Freeman and Watson, 1962, *Phys. Rev.*, **127**, 2058.)

complicated than the wide-multiplet case but it is similar in principle. The result is to give $Sm^{3+}$ and $Eu^{3+}$ susceptibility values which do not follow a simple Curie–Weiss law but which do agree well with experiment. In the absence of this effect $Eu^{3+}$ would have a paramagnetic susceptibility of zero, having a singlet ground state with $J = 0$. This is a case where the term $\alpha_J$ mentioned in Section 2.4 does contribute significantly.

### 2.4.3  *Experimental behaviour of transition series salts*

The experimental susceptibilities of metallic transition metals do not support the free ion theory at all. This is because the magnetic d-electrons are also involved to a varying degree in crystal bonding and conduction and the free ion model is not appropriate. For salts of the first transition series of elements, the agreement with the simple free ion theory is mostly rather poor. However, if it is assumed that orbital moment plays no part in the magnetism and that the moment is wholly for spin, experimental and calculated values of $p_{eff}$ agree quite well for many of these salts (see Fig. 2.9).

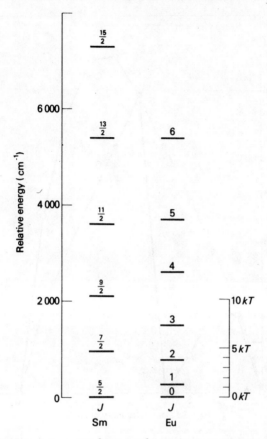

**Figure 2.8** Multiplet spacings of $Sm^{3+}$ and $Eu^{3+}$. The scale showing thermal energy is for a temperature of 300 K.

The value for $p_{eff}$ then becomes $p_{eff} = 2[S(S+1)]^{\frac{1}{2}}$, since when $L = 0$, $g$ has the value 2.

The reason for this loss of orbital moment is that the magnetic electrons in transition series ions are not screened by significant distributions of charge. The partly filled 3d-shells feel the effect of anisotropic crystalline electric fields produced by their environment. In the first transition series the effects of crystal field are stronger than those of spin–orbit coupling, although not so strong as to break down the couplings which operate in isolated atoms to set up the resultant vectors $S$ and $L$. This contrasts with the behaviour of rare-earth ions, where the spin–orbit coupling is stronger than the crystal field effects.

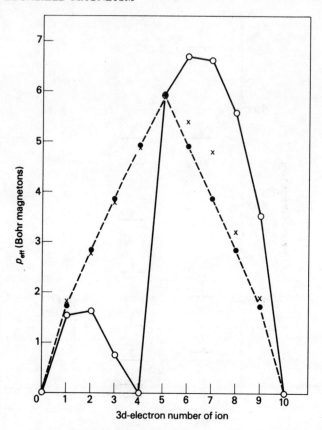

**Figure 2.9** Experimental and calculated values of $p_{\text{eff}}$ for ions of the first transition series. ×, experiment; ○ and full line, calculated for full $J$; ● and broken line, calculated for spin only.

The crystal field exerts its greatest influence on the direction of the orbital angular momentum. It does not interact directly with electron spin. In an atom, differing values of the atomic quantum numbers $L$ and $M_L$ correspond to different spatial distributions of electronic charge, and when $L$ is not equal to zero these are not spherically symmetrical. They spread out in various directions in the form of lobes and other shapes. In the free atom, when no magnetic field is applied, there is no reason to distinguish between the directions of the different orbital distributions. In a solid crystal other ions surround the atom in question and set up an electrostatic field. Those lobes of charge which point towards neighbouring atoms (regarded as point charges) correspond to higher energies than those which point between atoms. What in free space would be a degenerate situation involving different $M_L$ states is split in the crystal into fairly widely separated energy levels. The kind of splitting depends on the symmetry of the crystal and not all the orbital degeneracy is necessarily removed. Lower symmetry generally leads to more splitting. The crystal field exerts a torque on the orbital momentum so that it is not constant in direction. The result is that the mean values of the components of the orbital momentum in the three Cartesian directions average out in many cases to zero. When a magnetic field is applied the components still have mean values which are zero and the orbital contribution to the whole magnetic moment is nil. This is known as quenching of the orbital magnetic moment. When the orbital moment is totally quenched only spin moment contributes.

The crystal field effects in salts of the elements of the first transition series produce energy intervals of the order of $10^4$ cm$^{-1}$. The much weaker spin–orbit coupling then acts as a small perturbation, resulting in a weak polarization of the orbital wavefunctions. This causes the mean value of the orbital momentum no longer to be exactly zero and produces a small orbital contribution to the magnetic moment. The $g$ factor differs from the spin-only value of two; and this gives the mechanism whereby a mainly spin-type magnetic moment is coupled with the directionality of the crystal.

Sometimes the orbital moment is not completely quenched and a degenerate orbital ground state remains. This is acted upon and split by spin–orbit coupling into clearly separated states not far apart compared with the thermal energy $kT$. The observed susceptibility then deviates from the Curie (or Curie–Weiss) law at relatively low temperatures, but often approaches this law at high temperatures.

### 2.4.4 Direct measurement of the g factor

At the beginning of this chapter, reference was made to the magnetomechanical ratio $\gamma$, and values were given for pure orbital motion and for pure electron spin. More generally, $\gamma = -(e/2m)g$ and direct measurement of $\gamma$ can lead to experimental values for $g$ which may be compared with the values predicted by application of Hund's rules.

The direct experiment to measure $\gamma$ in paramagnetic materials consists of applying a magnetic field to a specimen of the solid containing the magnetic ions and then measuring the gross change in angular momentum of the whole specimen produced by the magnetomechanical interaction of the electrons. The experiment was carried out for a number of rare earth and first transition series paramagnetic compounds by Sucksmith between 1930 and 1932.

A resonance method was used in which the specimen was suspended and acted upon by a slowly alternating magnetic field, the frequency of which was equal to the natural frequency of the suspended system. Values of $\gamma$ and therefore of $g$ were derived from the amplitude of the oscillation produced. It was one of the most delicate and skilful experiments ever carried out in magnetism.

**Table 2.1**  Magnetomechanical measurements of $g$-factor.

| Material | Paramagnetic ion | Ground state | Calculated $g$ | | Experimental $g$ |
|---|---|---|---|---|---|
| | | | Full $J$ | Spin only | |
| Rare-earth ions | | | | | |
| $Nd_2O_3$ | $Nd^{3+}$ | $^4I_{5/2}$ | 0·73 | | 0·78 |
| $Gd_2O_3$ | $Gd^{3+}$ | $^8S_{7/2}$ | 2·00 | | 2·12 |
| $Dy_2O_3$ | $Dy^{3+}$ | $^6H_{15/2}$ | 1·33 | | 1·36 |
| First transition series ions | | | | | |
| $CrCl_3$ | $Cr^{3+}$ | $^4F_{3/2}$ | 0·40 | 2·00 | 1·95 |
| $MnSO_4$ | $Mn^{2+}$ | $^6S_{5/2}$ | 2·00 | 2·00 | 1·98 |
| $FeSO_4$ | $Fe^{2+}$ | $^5D_4$ | 1·50 | 2·00 | 1·89 |
| $CoSO_4$ | $Co^{2+}$ | $^4F_{9/2}$ | 1·33 | 2·00 | 1·54 |

The results (see Table 2.1) confirmed the predictions of the Hund theory for rare earths and showed that indeed spin moment is dominant for ions of the first transition series.

Complementary measurements using microwave resonance techniques have been made more recently. They support the same conclusions.

## 2.5   Ferromagnetism in the local moment model

A ferromagnetic sample is usually divided up into domains which are spontaneously magnetized nearly or completely to saturation. Applied magnetic fields can change the direction of the magnetization within the domains but, except in certain circumstances, they can make little difference to its magnitude. The magnetization within the domain is called the intrinsic magnetization $\sigma_{B,T}$ (per unit mass at temperature $T$) and its value in zero field is the spontaneous magnetization $\sigma_{0,T}$. The saturation magnetization $\sigma_{0,0}$ is the value of $\sigma_{0,T}$ at zero temperature.

A basic explanation of the occurrence of the spontaneous magnetization was derived from the postulate put forward by Weiss in 1907 that an intense internal or molecular magnetic field exists within the ferromagnetic solid. This was assumed to act upon each atomic magnetic moment and to be proportional in magnitude to the magnetization of the part of the solid immediately surrounding the moment in question. The magnitude of this field was typically of the order of $10^3$ T (or $10^7$ Oe). Weiss realized that such a strong field could not be provided by purely magnetic effects such as dipole fields. It is now recognized as being a convenient way of treating interatomic interaction effects, which can be represented as though they are equivalent to an internal magnetic field. While the Weiss model in its simplest form was very successful in explaining the existence of a ferromagnetic state, it is known now that the materials to which it was first applied, metallic iron, nickel and cobalt, are not good examples of ionic ferromagnets. Their magnetism is not strongly localized in the ion cores. The rare earth elements are better examples.

The justification for the assumption that the molecular field is proportional to the local magnetization is the expectation that the driving force tending to align an atomic moment in the same direction as that of its neighbourhood will depend on what proportion of its neighbours are already aligned. The magnetization of the neighbourhood is a measure of this.

What was called the applied field $B_0$ in the treatment of ionic paramagnetism now becomes the sum of the internal and the applied fields, $(B_0)_i + B_0$.

If $N_s$ is the number of atoms per kilogramme of specimen ($= 1000\,N/M$, where $N$ is Avogadro's number and $M$ is the molar weight of the substance), the intrinsic magnetization per unit mass

$$\sigma_{B,T} = N_s \langle \mu_{J\uparrow} \rangle$$

We write

$$(B_0)_i = \gamma_m \sigma_{B,T} = N_s \gamma_m \langle \mu_{J\uparrow} \rangle$$

where $\gamma_m$ is a constant of proportionality called the molecular field coefficient.

### 2.5.1  Calculation of the spontaneous magnetization

We now include the molecular field in the theory given already for the paramagnetic case. The quantity abbreviated as $y$ becomes

$$y' = J\, g\, \mu_B (B_0 + N_s \gamma_m \langle \mu_{J\uparrow} \rangle)/kT$$

and we look again for a solution for $\langle \mu_{J\uparrow} \rangle$.

As before, but writing $y'$ for $y$

$$\langle \mu_{J\uparrow} \rangle / J\, g\, \mu_B = \sigma_{B,T}/\sigma_{0,0} = F(J, y') \tag{2.8}$$

Now the solution is less obvious than before, since $\langle \mu_{J\uparrow} \rangle$ appears on

both sides of the equation. When we deal with the spontaneous
magnetization $\sigma_{0,T}$ then $B_0 = 0$. That is,

$$y' = J g \mu_B N_s \gamma_m \langle \mu_{J\uparrow} \rangle / kT$$

or,

$$\langle \mu_{J\uparrow} \rangle / J g \mu_B = \sigma_{0,T} / \sigma_{0,0} = [kT/N_s \gamma_m (J g \mu_B)^2] y' \tag{2.9}$$

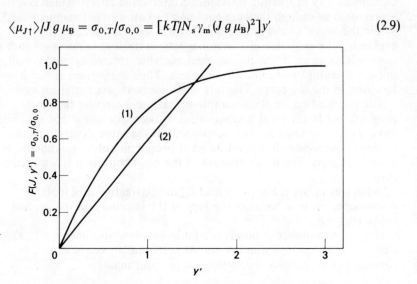

**Figure 2.10** Solution of equations 2.8 (line 1) and 2.9 (line 2) to obtain the spontaneous
magnetization of a ferromagnet.

The curves of equations 2.8 and 2.9 are shown in Fig. 2.10. The solution
sought is clearly the non-zero intersection of lines (1) and (2).

The position of curve (1) is independent of temperature. The slope of
curve (2) is proportional to $T$. As the slope of curve (2) increases with
rising temperature, the solution for the reduced magnetization represented
by the ordinate of the intersection decreases and becomes zero when the
slope of curve (2) exceeds the initial slope of curve (1). The temperature at
which the magnetization becomes zero is the ferromagnetic Curie
temperature $T_C$.

The calculated variation of the reduced spontaneous magnetization with
temperature is shown in Fig. 2.11. The exact form of the curve depends
somewhat on $J$. The result agrees roughly with experiment, but this is not
a very sensitive test of the theory.

Similarly the calculation may be extended to give the expected
dependence of intrinsic magnetization on field at different temperatures

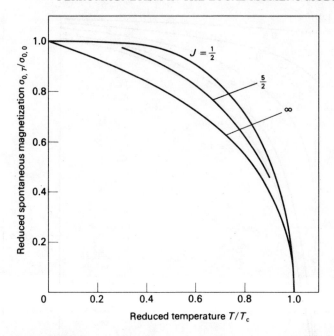

**Figure 2.11** Calculated reduced curves of spontaneous magnetization plotted against temperature for $J = \frac{1}{2}, \frac{5}{2}$ and $\infty$.

(Fig. 1.3). Finite values of $B_0$ are included so that Equ. 2.9 becomes

$$\langle \mu_{J\uparrow} \rangle / J g \mu_B = A T y' - C \tag{2.10}$$

where $A = k/[N_s \gamma_m (J g \mu_B)^2]$ and $C = B_0 / (N_s \gamma_m J g \mu_B)$. Simultaneous solution of equations 2.8 and 2.10 gives values of intrinsic magnetization for varying field at chosen fixed temperatures, as shown in Fig. 2.12. This is broadly similar to experiment (Fig. 1.3) but the detailed agreement is not good for metallic ferromagnets.

### 2.5.2   Relationship between the molecular field coefficient and the Curie temperature

Since the existence of a ferromagnetic state depends on the magnetic interactions represented by the molecular field, it is to be expected that a close relationship will exist between the molecular field coefficient $\gamma_m$ and the Curie Temperature $T_C$ at which the ferromagnetic state breaks down.

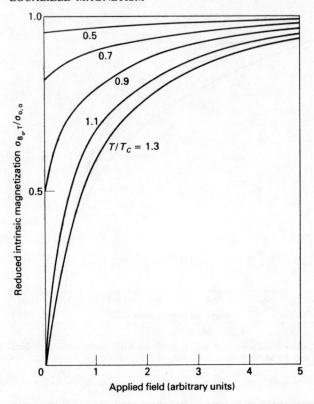

**Figure 2.12** Calculated dependence of reduced intrinsic magnetization on applied field for $J = \frac{1}{2}$.

When no field is applied and at temperatures immediately below $T_C$ the magnetization and therefore $y'$ are small. The approximate form of the Brillouin function may be used:

$$F(J,y') = \sigma_{0,T}/\sigma_{0,0} = (J+1)\,y'/3J$$

Also (Equ. 2.9 above)

$$\sigma_{0,T}/\sigma_{0,0} = k\,T\,y'/[N_s\gamma_m(J\,g\mu_B)^2]$$

That is, when $T = T_C$

$$\gamma_m = 3\,k\,T_C/[J(J+1)g^2\,\mu_B^2\,N_s]$$

As an example, for metallic gadolinium,

$$T_C = 293\,\text{K}; \quad J = \tfrac{7}{2}; \quad g = 2; \quad \text{atomic weight} = M = 157.3$$

Also,

$$N = 6.023 \times 10^{23}\,\text{mol}^{-1}; \; \mu_B = 9.273 \times 10^{-24}\,\text{J}\,\text{T}^{-1};$$
$$k = 1.381 \times 10^{-23}\,\text{J}\,\text{K}^{-1}$$

Thus

$$\gamma_m \simeq 0\cdot 6\,\text{J}^{-1}\,\text{T}^2\,\text{kg}$$

The saturation magnetization of metallic Gd is

$$\sigma_{0,0} = 268\,\text{J}\,\text{T}^{-1}\,\text{kg}^{-1}$$

The molecular field at $T = 0$ is therefore expected to be

$$\gamma_m \sigma_{0,0} = 157\,\text{T}\,(= 1.57 \times 10^6\,\text{Oe})$$

$\gamma_m$ may also be estimated in other ways. Relatively small differences occur between the different estimates, mostly because of deficiencies in the model used.

### 2.5.3  Susceptibility above the Curie temperature

At temperatures above the Curie temperature the magnetization is small and the molecular field is of the same order as the applied field. Again we may write

$$F(J,y') = \langle \mu_{J\uparrow} \rangle / J\, g\, \mu_B = (J+1)\, y'/3J$$

Also,

$$y' = J\, g\, \mu_B (B_0 + N_s \gamma_m \langle \mu_{J\uparrow} \rangle)/kT$$

Thus,

$$N_s \langle \mu_{J\uparrow} \rangle = N_s J(J+1) g^2 \mu_B^2 (B_0 + N_s \gamma_m \langle \mu_{J\uparrow} \rangle)/3\,kT$$

The susceptibility $\chi$ is the gross moment divided by the field. That is,

$$\chi = N_s \langle \mu_{J\uparrow} \rangle / B_0 = C/(T - \theta_p) \tag{2.11}$$

where $C = N_s p_{\text{eff}}^2/3k$, $\theta_p = N_s \gamma_m p_{\text{eff}}^2/3k$ and $p_{\text{eff}}^2 = g^2 \mu_B^2 J(J+1)$.
  This is the Curie–Weiss law.
  $\theta_p$ is identical in this treatment to the quantity $T_C$ derived already. Experimentally, $\theta_p$ is usually slightly greater than $T_C$.
  If the molar susceptibility is calculated instead, $\chi_m = C_m/(T - \theta_p)$, where $C_m = N p_{\text{eff}}^2/3k$.
  This value $C_m$ is the same as the one calculated previously for non-interacting ions.

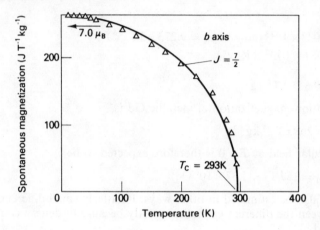

**Figure 2.13** Spontaneous magnetization measured along the $b$-axis in the basal plane of single crystal gadolinium, compared with calculation for $J = \frac{7}{2}$. (After Nigh, Legvold and Spedding, 1963, *Phys. Rev.*, **132**, 1092.)

### 2.5.4 *Comparison with experiment*

The only rare earth metal which is a simple ferromagnet is gadolinium. The ionic (localized moment) model described here fits its basic magnetic properties quite well. The measured saturation magnetization is equivalent to a moment of $7.55$ $\mu_B$ per atom. This compares with the value $7.0$ $\mu_B$ expected for the 4f-moment of a state ${}^8S_{7/2}$. The difference is thought to be due to an additional polarization of electrons more closely associated with conduction and related to the outermost atomic energy levels. The shape of the curve of intrinsic magnetization against temperature is reasonably close to that calculated for $J = S = \frac{7}{2}$ (Fig. 2.13). The Curie–Weiss law is followed well by the susceptibility above the Curie temperature; and the experimental value for $p_{eff}$ is $7.98$ compared with the theoretical value of $7.94$ for the ${}^8S_{7/2}$ state. It is notable that the excess moment attributed to outer electrons does not occur in the paramagnetic state.

For ferromagnetic transition metals and also their alloys the agreement is less satisfactory. Above the Curie temperature the susceptibility often follows a Curie–Weiss law approximately. But there are many examples of graphs of $\chi^{-1}$ against $T$ which are curved. Measured values of $p_{eff}$ do not correlate either with the ionic theory or with the saturation magnetization. The moment per atom derived from the saturation magnetization is usually a non-integral multiple of the Bohr magneton; and there is no simple way in which this may be rationalized in the ionic theory.

# 3

# Magnetism Associated with Band Electrons

In Chapter 2 we considered the magnetism of electrons that may be treated as though they are contained within the cores of atoms in solids. There the requirement for a paramagnetic or ferromagnetic state was the existence of incompletely filled inner shells of electrons. The paramagnetic susceptibility found in these circumstances varies markedly with temperature.

Among the metallic elements there are many that are much less stongly paramagnetic and which show a susceptibility varying little or not at all with temperature (see Fig. 1.10). Examples are the alkali metals. All of them, Li, Na, K, Rb and Cs, show a similar temperature-independent weak paramagnetism. Their atoms do not contain incomplete inner electron shells. The explanation is based on the paramagnetism of a gas of electrons free to move throughout the space occupied by the metal. The electrons also provide a bonding mechanism for the metal as a whole.

Metallic transition elements form an intermediate group, in the main. Electrons in incomplete inner shells can take part in bonding and they are described by energy bands of finite width, rather than by discrete energy levels.

## 3.1 Paramagnetic susceptibility of free electrons

As a first approximation we consider a model in which the conduction electrons are assumed to be free and only constrained by the potential box formed by the external dimensions of the whole specimen. Since the size of the box is large compared with atomic dimensions the available energy levels of the electrons are very closely spaced and effectively continuous.

A simple quantum mechanical treatment shows that the density of electron states $v(E)$ varies parabolically with the energy $E$.

$$v(E) = (dz/dE)_E = 4\pi \, V \, (2m/h^2)^{3/2} \, E^{1/2} \tag{3.1}$$

where $V$ is the volume of the potential box, $h$ is Planck's constant, $m$ is the electron states $v(E)$ varies parabolically with the energy $E$.

This is the number of states, which on average may be filled with up to two electrons per state, one of each direction of spin. At $T = 0$ and when no field is applied there are two electrons per state at all energies up to the limiting Fermi energy $E_m$, no electrons having higher energies.

The number of electrons per state (both spin directions) is given by

$$2f(E) = 2 \{\exp[(E - \eta)/kT] + 1\}^{-1}$$

$\eta$ is a numerical factor equal to the Fermi energy $E_m$ at $T = 0$. At room temperature $kT/E_m$ is of the order of $10^{-2}$ and at all temperatures encountered in dealing with the metallic state $\eta$ differs very little from $E_m$. The variation of $2f$ with $E$ is shown in Fig. 3.1.

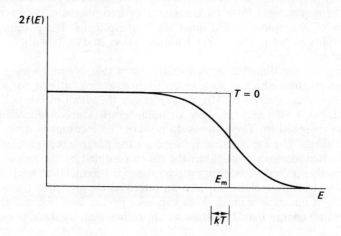

**Figure 3.1** Fermi–Dirac function $2f(E)$ plotted as a function of the energy $E$, for zero temperature and for a finite temperature $T$. The magnitude of the thermal energy $kT$ is indicated.

When an external field $B_0$ is applied to the metal the magnetic energy of a conduction electron can be either of two values; $-B_0\mu_B$ if the spin points parallel to the field and $+B_0\mu_B$ if it points antiparallel. Since $dz = v(E)\,dE$ is the number of electron states per unit volume in the range of energy from $E$ to $(E + dE)$ the number of electrons (one to each state) with spin parallel to the field is

$$v(E - B_0\mu_B)\,dE$$

and the number antiparallel is

$$v(E + B_0\mu_B)\,dE$$

The magnetic moment per unit volume is then

$$M = \mu_B \int_0^{E_m} (v(E + B_0\mu_B) - v(E - B_0\mu_B))dE$$

$$= \mu_B \int_{E_m - B_0\mu_B}^{E_m + B_0\mu_B} v(E)\,dE$$

Even in very strong fields $B_0\mu_B/E_m$ will only be of the order of $10^{-3}$, and the magnetization becomes

$$M = 2\mu_B^2 B_0\, v(E_m)$$

The susceptibility per unit volume at $T = 0$ is then

$$\kappa_0 = M/B_0 = 2\mu_B^2\, v(E_m) \tag{3.2}$$

Thus the susceptibility is a measure of the density of electron states at the Fermi level. So far the result is independent of any assumption concerning how good an approximation to the actual band structure is provided by the parabolic density of states of the free-electron model.

When the temperature is different from zero the filling of the states must be considered and the magnetization becomes

$$M = \mu_B \int f(E)\, v(E)\,dE$$

For the free-electron gas the volume susceptibility is now approximately equal to

$$\kappa = \kappa_0[1 - (\pi^2/12)(kT/E_m)^2 + \ldots] \tag{3.3}$$

Since $kT$ is always very much less than $E_m$ this is a very small decrease with increasing temperature. The susceptibility of a free-electron gas is essentially independent of temperature.

### 3.1.1 Comparison with experiment

In actual metals the free-electron model does not hold exactly and the density of states differs from a simple parabolic form (see Coles and Caplin, 1976, The Electronic Structures of Solids, Arnold, London). In the least complicated case of the alkali metals the deviation can be taken into account by the introduction of a calculated electron effective mass $m^*$.

Before the results of the theory can be compared with experiment various other effects must be allowed for. Electron–electron interactions (exchange and correlation) occur, although for heavier elements their influence is not known very accurately. Correction for diamagnetism is also necessary. The diamagnetic effect of the ion core increases considerably as the atomic number increases although it remains relatively small. There is another effect called the Landau diamagnetism. It describes the orientation of the quantized orbital angular momenta in the external magnetic field. For free electrons its absolute magnitude is one third of the paramagnetic susceptibility due to spin, but it is influenced considerably by changes in effective mass.

**Table 3.1**  Experimental and calculated mass susceptibilities of alkali metals.

|    | Experiment | | Theory | | |
|----|------------|------------|------------|------------|------------|
|    | (a) $\chi_{total}$ | (b) $\chi_{spin}$ | (c) $\chi_p$ | (d) $\chi_p(corr)$ | (e) $\chi_{total}$ |
| Li | 3·60 | 3·83 | 1·44 | 4.00 | 3.60 |
| Na | 0·61 | 1·12 | 0·65 | 0·85 | 0·42 |
| K  | 0·46 | —    | 0·59 | 0·81 | 0·24 |
| Rb | 0·20 | —    | 0·30 | 0·49 | 0·11 |
| Cs | 0·26 | —    | 0·23 | 0·57 | 0·23 |

All are units of $10^{-2} \, J \, T^{-2} \, kg^{-1}$ SI or $10^{-6} \, erg \, Oe^{-2} \, g^{-1}$ CGS.

Table 3.1 shows the mass susceptibilities of alkali metals. The first column (a) gives the experimental value of the total susceptibility. The second column (b) gives available values of the spin susceptibility, not subject to diamagnetic effects and derived from magnetic resonance experiments. The remaining columns give the theoretical estimates: (c) free-electron paramagnetic susceptibility (Pauli); (d) susceptibility corrected for effective mass, exchange and correlation; and (e) corrected for diamagnetism. The agreement respectively between columns (b) and (d); and between (a) and (e) is tolerably good.

For other metals that are less simple than the alkalis the theory is more difficult. The effective masses in such metals are anisotropic and often show large variations. The band shape is usually far from the simple parabolic form. And in many cases the effect of exchange is strong. Most transition metals, with unfilled inner electron shells represented by bands of relatively high density of states, are much more strongly paramagnetic than the alkali metals, and their susceptibility usually depends significantly on temperature.

## 3.2  Ferromagnetism of band electrons

In the same way that a ferromagnetic state was explained by taking the ionic model of paramagnetism and introducing a molecular field representing the exchange interactions, ferromagnetism appears when an internal field is introduced into the treatment of the paramagnetism of an electron gas. The first simple treatment of this model was made by Stoner, who named it 'Collective electron ferromagnetism'.

The system considered is effectively the same as the model for free-electron paramagnetism.

(a) There is a set of $N$ electrons in a partially filled electronic energy band in which the energy density of states $v(E)$ is given as before by

$$v(E) = dz/dE = 4\pi \ V \ (2m/h^2)^{3/2} E^{1/2}$$

If the electrons exist in balance pairs in their lowest energy states their maximum energy is $E_m$. The total number of states filled by $N$ electrons (two per state) up to the maximum energy is

$$\tfrac{1}{2}N = z = 4\pi \ V \ (2m/h^2)^{3/2} \tfrac{2}{3}E_m^{\ 3/2}$$

Thus

$$v(E) = dz/dE = \tfrac{3}{4}(N/E_m^{\ 3/2})E^{1/2} \tag{3.4}$$

Alternatively, $N$ may be the number of electron holes in a nearly full band, the energy then being measured from the top of the band downwards. The effective mass would be different from that for free electrons. The number $N$ corresponds to $p$ electrons (or holes) per atom, and $p$ is not necessarily integral. The lack of a need for integral values of $p$ is one of the greatest merits of this theory. In nickel the value of $p$ is known from experiment to be about 0·6, this corresponding to the number of holes in the 3d-band. This is illustrated in Fig. 3.2.

That the band is parabolic, as for free electrons, is a simplifying assumption although variations in the band shape make little difference to the main conclusions of the theory. Changes in electron effective mass are taken into account within the value of $E_m$. In general in transition metals the magnetically significant parts of the d-bands are relatively narrow, certainly less than 1 eV wide.

(b) Exchange interaction is introduced in the form of a molecular field proportional to the average magnetization. It is convenient in this treatment to express it so that its effect on the energy of electrons with spin respectively antiparallel and parallel to the magnetization is $+ k\theta' \zeta$

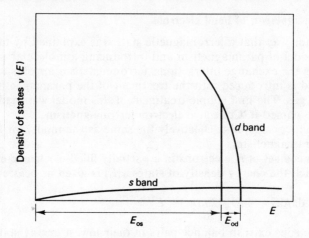

**Figure 3.2** Diagrammatic representation of the band structure of nickel near the Fermi level.

or $-k\theta'\zeta$, where $\zeta$ is the relative magnetization $\sigma_{B_0,T}/\sigma_{0,0}$, and $\theta'$ is the molecular field parameter expressed with the dimensions of temperature (analogous to the Curie temperature).

(c) The distribution of electrons in the band depends on temperature, applied field $B_0$ and the molecular field, and may now be calculated by the application of Fermi–Dirac statistics.

The total number of electrons $N$ in the band must be equal to the sum of the numbers $N^+$ and $N^-$ having the two spin directions:

$$N^+ = \int_0^\infty (dz/dE)f(E-E')\,dE$$

$$= \int_0^\infty dz/dE)\,\{\exp[(E-E'-\eta)/kT]+1\}^{-1}\,dE \tag{3.5}$$

and

$$N^- = \int_0^\infty (dz/dE)\,\{\exp[(E+E'-\eta)/kT]+1\}^{-1}\,dE \tag{3.6}$$

If we write

$$\eta' = \eta/kT$$

$$\beta = k\theta'\zeta/kT\,;\ \beta' = \mu_{\mathrm B}B_0/kT$$

(The field $B_0$ and the magnetization, and hence $\beta$ and $\beta'$, always have the same sign.)

$$\beta + \beta' = E'/kT$$
$$x = E/kT$$

so that

$$E^{1/2}dE = (kT)^{3/2}x^{1/2}dx$$

as we saw earlier,

$$dz/dE = v(E) = \tfrac{3}{4}(N/E_m^{3/2})E^{1/2}$$

then

$$N = \tfrac{3}{4}N\,(kT/E_m)^{3/2}\,[F_{\frac{1}{2}}(\eta' + \beta + \beta') + F_{\frac{1}{2}}(\eta' - \beta - \beta')] \tag{3.7}$$

Equ. 3.7 serves to fix the parameter $\eta'$ (and hence $\eta$) in the Fermi–Dirac function $f(E)$. The integral

$$F_{\frac{1}{2}}(\varepsilon) = \int_0^\infty x^{1/2}[\exp(x-\varepsilon)+1]^{-1}\,dx$$

is one of a set of Fermi–Dirac integrals, the values of which have been determined numerically and are available in tabulated form.

Likewise the magnetization is

$$M = \tfrac{3}{4}N\,(kT/E_m)^{3/2}\,[F_{\frac{1}{2}}(\eta' + \beta + \beta') - F_{\frac{1}{2}}(\eta' - \beta - \beta')] \tag{3.8}$$

This is the magnetization per unit volume. The magnetization per unit mass in field $B_0$ and at a temperature $T$ is given by $\sigma_{B0,T} = M/\rho$, where $\rho$ is the density.

The solution of these equations, which Stoner carried out numerically, leads to values of the magnetization (and the susceptibility) for varying conditions of applied field and temperature. Varying strengths of exchange interaction were considered. The results were expressed conveniently in a reduced, dimensionless, form.

### 3.2.1 The paramagnetic state

The reduced form of the susceptibility is

$$\zeta E_m/\mu_B B_0 = \chi E_m/\sigma_{0,0}\mu_B$$

since $\zeta = \sigma_{B_0,T}/\sigma_{0,0}$ is the reduced magnetization. The temperature is reduced by referring the thermal energy $kT$ to the maximum energy $E_m$.

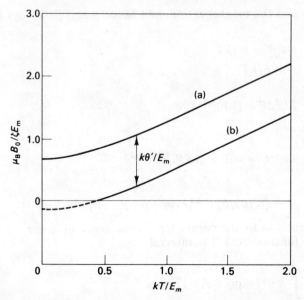

**Figure 3.3** Calculated reciprocal susceptibility; (a) without interaction and (b) with interaction. (After Stoner, 1951, *J. Physique*, **12**, 377.)

In Fig. 3.3, curve (a) shows the curve for no exchange interaction, $k\theta'/E_m = 0$. This is the same as the Pauli free-electron paramagnetism considered already. When $kT$ is small compared with $E_m$ the susceptibility is effectively independent of temperature. A metal to which the simple Pauli theory might apply will reach its melting temperature when $kT/E_m$ is about $10^{-2}$.

The effect of positive exchange interaction is to lower the curve by an amount $k\theta'/E_m$ (Fig. 3.3, curve (b)). If the lowered curve cuts the $T$ axis, the point of intersection corresponds to the Curie temperature $T_C$ and a ferromagnetic state exists at all lower temperatures. $T_C$ is always less than the interaction parameter $\theta'$, and a positive exchange interaction does not necessarily give rise to ferromagnetism. For a spontaneous ferromagnetic moment to occur $k\theta'/E_m$ must reach a critical value. This has been shown to be equal to 2/3 for a parabolic band. As the interaction parameter is further increased more and more electrons are transferred to the favoured spin direction, until eventually a saturation condition is reached. The remaining vacancies in the d-band are then only of one kind of spin, and no further transfer can take place without violating the Pauli exclusion principle. For this to occur $k\theta'/E_m$ must be at least $2^{-1/3} = 0.7937$.

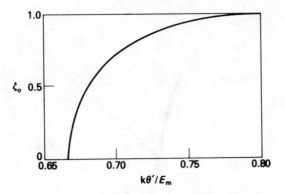

**Figure 3.4** Saturation of the ferromagnetic state. The dependence of the relative magnetization $\zeta_0$ at zero temperature on the interaction parameter $k\theta'/E_m$. (After Stoner, 1951, *J. Physique*, **12**, 377.)

When $k\theta'/E_m$ lies between $2/3 = 0\cdot6667$ and $2^{-1/3} = 0\cdot7937$ the reduced magnetization at $T = 0$ ($= \zeta_0$) is less than unity (Fig. 3.4).

Fig. 3.5 shows how the calculated reduced magnetization $\zeta$ and the reduced inverse susceptibility depend on temperature for various strengths of interaction. Above the Curie temperature the $(1/\chi, T)$ relationship sometimes shows curvature, so deviating from a Curie–Weiss law. This is found experimentally in some alloys, although the effect is a weak one.

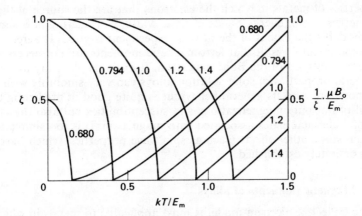

**Figure 3.5** Dependence on temperature of the calculated reduced magnetization (left) and reciprocal susceptibility (right) for different strengths of the interaction parameter. (After Stoner, 1951, *J. Physique*, **12**, 377.)

C

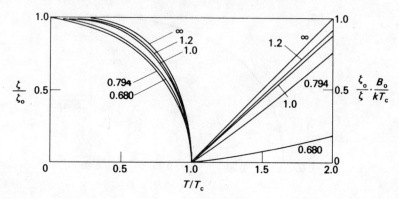

**Figure 3.6**  $\zeta/\zeta_0$ and calculated reciprocal susceptibility plotted against $T/T_C$. (After Stoner, 1951, *J. Physique*, **12**, 377.)

Under experimental conditions it would not be obvious when a value of the reduced magnetization $\zeta_0$ at $T = 0$ was less than unity. For purposes of comparison between theory and experiment, therefore, it is useful to calculate values of $\zeta/\zeta_0$ and to plot them against $T/T_C$ (Fig. 3.6). These curves agree fairly well with what is found experimentally in several alloy systems, for instance solid solutions of nickel containing increasing amounts of copper in solution (Fig. 3.7).

This model formed the basis of an understanding of the magnetic properties of metals in which the electrons that are the source of the magnetism are in energy bands of finite width. Considering how simple the model is the extent of the fit with experiment is good. It agrees with the experimental result that ferromagnetic moments are not necessarily integral multiples of the Bohr magneton. It explains plausibly how the magnetic properties of solid solution alloys can vary smoothly with alloy composition. And its general behaviour is quite good in predicting the detail of not only magnetizations and susceptibilities but also the thermal characteristics associated with magnetism. It is too simple to explain some other effects (such as spin wave properties) which have now been definitely established.

### 3.3  Magnetic moments of alloys

The collective electron model is most applicable to metals in which there is band overlap between electron energy bands, one of which is wide in energy and not very deep in density of states (relatively free electrons); and the other of which is narrow in energy and with a

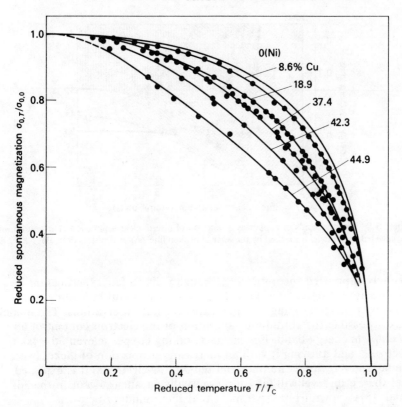

**Figure 3.7** Experimental curves of reduced magnetization plotted against reduced temperature for a series of nickel–copper alloys containing between 0 and 45 % of copper.

relatively high density of states. How this arises is shown in Fig. 3.8, which refers to copper. The Fermi energy is above the highest 3d-level and there are no vacancies in the 3d-band.

### 3.3.1  *The rigid-band model*

What follows depends on the applicability of the so-called 'rigid-band model'. This assumes that when two ('similar') elements that are not too far apart in the periodic table are alloyed together substitutionally in solid solution, their atoms contribute jointly to a common band structure. The Fermi level is then supposed to be determined by the concentration and effective valencies of the constituent elements, and their effect on the overall electron/atom ratio. The model is not very

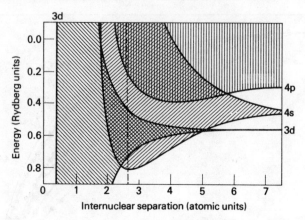

**Figure 3.8**   Energy bands of copper as a function of internuclear separation. The equilibrium distance between nuclei is marked by the vertical broken line. (After Krutter, 1935, *Phys. Rev.*, **48**, 664.)

strongly supported theoretically although it has a fair experimental justification. It must be used with caution; it is useful in leading to a first-order understanding of many experimental observations. The model makes possible the continuous alteration of the electron content of an incomplete energy band. For instance, taking copper (eleven 3d + 4s-electrons) and alloying it with an increasing proportion of nickel (with the next lower atomic number and ten 3d + 4s-electrons) it is expected that the Fermi level will fall until eventually vacancies occur in the 3d-band. It is known from experiment that the boundary between ferromagnetism and no ferromagnetism at $T = 0$ is at an alloy composition of about 53 at.% of copper and 47 at.% of nickel.

### 3.3.2  Nickel

The value for the saturation magnetization of pure nickel at $T = 0$ is $\sigma_{0,0} = 58 \cdot 6$ J $T^{-1}$ kg$^{-1}$ (see Table 7.3). This value is about $1 \cdot 6\%$ higher than the one measured by Weiss and Forrer (1926) and for long accepted as a standard. Thus in accepting old data on saturation magnetization it is necessary to find out what standard was used and where appropriate to apply a correction. The saturation magnetization of Ni is equivalent to a Bohr magneton number $p = gJ = 0 \cdot 616$. The best value for $g$ is 2.185. Thus the number of uncompensated spins per atom is $0 \cdot 563$. If the magnetic electrons are 3d-electrons and the 3d-band contains its full quota (five per atom) of electrons with positive spin, all the vacancies giving rise to the magnetic moment will be on the negative side. Since in nickel the total of 3d + 4s-electrons is ten, there must be 0·56 4s-electrons per atom in the metal. This number is slightly lower than the number of conduction electrons obtained from observations on the Hall effect, suggesting that 3d-electrons might contribute to conduction in nickel to a small degree, as well as 4s-electrons.

### 3.3.3  Cobalt

In pure cobalt a change of phase occurs near 400°C, the equilibrium crystal structure being face-centred cubic at temperatures above the change and close-packed hexagonal below. Both phases are ferromagnetic with high Curie temperatures, that of the cubic phase being above 1100°C. The hexagonal phase is strongly anisotropic magnetically. Its saturation magnetization, measured on single crystals oriented along their magnetic easy direction, is equivalent to a magneton number of 1·715 $\mu_B$. That of the cubic phase (extrapolated from measurements carried out at temperatures above the phase transformation) is 1.751 $\mu_B$. The g value is 2·170. Applying this g value to both phases gives differences in the number of positive and negative spins per atom of 1·61 and 1·58 for the cubic and hexagonal phases, respectively. The total number of 3d + 4s-electrons in cobalt is nine. There is no direct evidence to show the exact distribution of the electrons, but the changes in magnetic properties on alloying seem to point to the 3d positive sub-band having its full quota of five electrons, with about 1·6 vacancies per atom on the negative side.

### 3.3.4  Iron

The magneton number of body-centred cubic iron is 2·22 $\mu_B$. The g value is 2·094. Thus the difference between the numbers of positive and negative spins per atom is 2·12.

Again there is no direct evidence on the distribution of the outer electrons. However, the total number of 3d + 4s-electrons in iron is eight, and if all the 3d-vacancies were of the same sign there would only be 0·12 4s 'conduction' electrons per atom. This seems to be rather too small in comparison to the equivalent number for Cu, Ni and Co. In addition, alloying behaviour suggests that vacancies of both signs occur in the 3d-band, with roughly one electron per atom in the s-band.

Face-centred cubic pure iron is not stable below about 900°C, but when it is stabilized by the addition of various alloying elements it is non-ferromagnetic even at very low temperatures. It has been shown that an austenitic (face-centred cubic) steel containing 18·6% of Cr and 9% of Ni has a paramagnetic susceptibility which behaves in a way characteristic of an antiferromagnetic material below 40 K, and it has been inferred that if pure face-centred cubic iron existed at low enough temperatures, it would be antiferromagnetic.

At very high pressures iron has a close-packed hexagonal structure, and there are indications from the Mössbauer effect that it is not then magnetically ordered, although data for c.p.h. Fe–Ru alloys suggest that at normal atomic volume c.p.h. Fe may be antiferromagnetic.

Schematic density of states curves for nickel, cobalt and iron are shown in Fig. 3.9. The split in energy between 3d positive and negative sub-bands indicates the size of the exchange interaction, as measured by $T_C$.

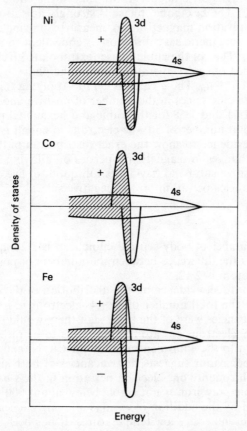

**Figure 3.9**  Schematic density of states graphs for nickel, cobalt and iron. The energy splitting between + and − directions is a measure of the exchange energy.

### 3.3.5  Face-centred cubic nickel–copper and cobalt–copper alloys

Copper dissolves in nickel continuously over the whole range of composition and extrapolates to $p = 0$ at 53 at.% of copper, where the magnetization (and therefore the magneton number) varies linearly with composition and extrapolates to $p = 0$ at 53 at. % of copper, where the mean number of 3d + 4s-electrons is 10·53. The $g$ value of nickel–copper alloys is substantially independent of composition and equal to the value for pure nickel. The average number of uncompensated spins per atom of the alloy thus varies linearly with composition. The Curie temperature $T_C$ also varies linearly with composition, from 631 K for pure nickel to zero at the composition where the magneton number falls to zero.

The experimental behaviour is therefore in broad agreement with the simple rigid-band model. One difficulty is that copper-rich nickel–copper alloys are strongly paramagnetic in spite of the vacant holes in the 3d-band having apparently been filled. This is because the model is too simple and there is not an absolutely uniform magnetic state on an atomic scale throughout the metal. There are other difficulties of detail when an exact comparison between experiment and the basic collective electron model is made.

In the case of cobalt–copper alloys there are experimental difficulties in that the solubility of cobalt in copper is only about 9 at.% and also the phase constitution is less simple. However, the rate of change of magneton number with composition has been measured. It is equivalent to a variation of the number of uncompensated spins per atom with total number of 3d + 4s-electrons per atom of 1·04 spins per electron. This number coincides with the equivalent quantity for nickel–copper alloys, again agreeing with the rigid-band model.

### 3.3.6  Other alloys of nickel and cobalt

Several elements in the central groups of the periodic table form substitutional alloys with nickel and cobalt, and it is generally supposed that they can act as donors of electrons to the structure. If it is assumed that the loosely bound electrons ('valence' electrons) outside the inner closed shells in the atoms of the solute elements are available for transfer to the vacant states in the 3d-band of the solvent, correlation is expected between the rate of change of magneton number $p$ with composition $c$ and the normal valency $q$ of the solute. Such agreement is found experimentally. Higher solute valency corresponds to faster rate of decrease $dp/dc$ of the magneton number. The quantity $(1/q)dp/dc$ is approximately constant for a number of binary alloys based on nickel, as is shown in Table 3.2.

**Table 3.2** Dependence of rate of dilution of magnetic moment $dp/dc$ on the valency $q$ of the solute element in binary nickel alloys.

| Solute element | Valency | $dp/dc$ | $(1/q)dp/dc$ |
|---|---|---|---|
| Cu | 1 | 1·14 | 1·14 |
| Zn | 2 | 2·11 | 1·06 |
| Al | 3 | 2·80 | 0·93 |
| Si | 4 | 3·77 | 0·94 |
| Ge | 4 | 3·70 | 0·93 |
| Sn | 4 | 4·22 | 1·06 |
| Sb | 5 | 5.31 | 1·06 |

A limited number of alloys based on face-centred cubic cobalt show broadly similar behaviour, but the numerical correlation is much poorer.

Relatively few non-transition elements form extensive solid solutions based on iron in the body-centred cubic phase. Those that do form solutions simply act magnetically as diluents and leave the magnetic moment per iron atom unchanged. Elements that act in this way are aluminium, silicon and tin. There is no evidence to distinguish between whether the solute supplies electrons in equal numbers to offset vacancies in the 3d-band of iron which are probably present for electrons with either spin, or whether the solute supplies no electrons at all to the iron 3d-band.

### 3.3.7 Face-centred cubic binary alloys between transition elements

Wide ranges of solid solution exist in many of the alloys between elements of the first transition series. In Fig. 3.10 the mean number of uncompensated spins per atom, derived from the experimental values of magneton numbers and $g$ factors, is plotted against the average number of 3d + 4s-electrons per atom, for several such alloy systems. The data for nickel–copper and cobalt–copper alloys are included in the diagram.

The outstanding feature of this graph is that over wide ranges of composition the data for many systems lie exactly on the straight line drawn between the points for pure nickel and for pure cobalt. These systems include nickel–copper, nickel–iron, nickel–cobalt, cobalt–copper and cobalt–iron.

Deviations from the common line occur whenever the solute has a lower atomic number than that of iron and also when the solute is iron if its concentration is high.

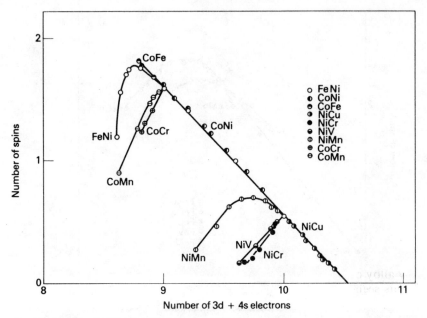

**Figure 3.10** Number of magnetic electron spins per atom plotted against the average number of (3d + 4s)-electrons per atom for face-centred cubic binary alloys.

The occurrence of this common straight line having a slope near to unity is regarded as supporting the application of the rigid-band model to those systems which lie on it. The picture is of a common 3d-band shared by both elements present, the Fermi level varying as the average electron density changes with varying composition. Such a description would seem to apply at the top of the 3d-band and for elements of atomic number not less than that of iron. It could be seen as a consequence of the spatial overlap between 3d-like charge distributions of neighbouring atoms being strongest where the ion cores are largest.

Where deviations from the common line occur it would seem that the smaller ions are reacting individually. Since they do not appear to act as simple diluents to the magnetization of the solvent, they seem therefore to possess magnetic moments of their own, which are at least partially aligned by interaction with the solvent atoms. The existence of localized characteristic magnetic moments on solute atoms has been confirmed in a few of these cases by neutron diffraction.

In some of those alloys in which deviations from the common line occur most rapidly the existence of an antiferromagnetic state at higher solute contents has been either confirmed or is suspected. For instance,

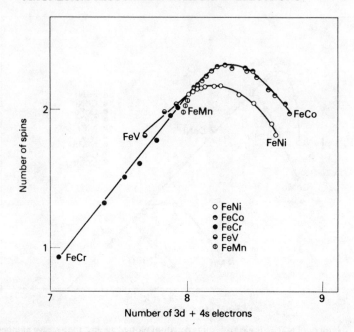

**Figure 3.11** Number of magnetic electron spins per atom plotted against the average number of (3d + 4s)-electrons per atom for body-centred cubic binary alloys.

antiferromagnetism occurs in the nickel–manganese system and is suspected in the face-centred cubic phase of the nickel–iron system at high iron concentrations. It may be that the steepness of the line is somehow related to the onset of an antiferromagnetic state.

When body-centred cubic alloys are similarly examined, Fig. 3.11 is obtained. In this crystal structure, no overlap occurs between data for different alloy systems even for solutes in iron which are neighbouring elements. Here there seems to be no question of both kinds of atom in a binary alloy contributing to a common 3d-band. Their magnetic moments seem always to act individually.

# 4

# Antiferromagnetism, Ferrimagnetism and Helimagnetism

## 4.1 Antiferromagnetism

Antiferromagnetism is a state in which the atomic magnetic moments in a solid are ideally highly aligned as they are in a perfect ferromagnet; but the individual moments are arranged in a self-compensatory way so that there is no overall spontaneous magnetization.

As we have seen already in Chapters 2 and 3, ferromagnetism occurs when there is a positive exchange interaction which may be described as a molecular field in the same direction as the local magnetization in the neighbourhood of a magnetic centre. The idea that the remaining non-ferromagnetic members of the first transition (3d) series of elements (Mn, Cr, V, Ti, Sc) might have negative interactions led to a theoretical study of the properties of antiferromagnetic systems. Néel (between 1932 and 1936) was the first to show that such a system has a critical temperature, now called the Néel temperature $T_N$, below which the atomic moments are arranged alternately parallel and antiparallel. Above $T_N$ the moments are disordered paramagnetically, as in a ferromagnet above $T_C$. It is now known that the metals to which the first ideas were applied do not necessarily exhibit the simple antiferromagnetism envisaged. The first clear experimental confirmation of antiferromagnetism was in non-metallic materials of an ionic kind, about 1950 or just before.

The simplest type of antiferromagnet is one in which the crystal may be divided into two sublattices, A and B, so that if the spins of one sublattice point one way, those of the other point the opposite way. The spins of atoms which are nearest neighbours are always antiparallel. Simple cubic and body-centred cubic crystal structures may fit this requirement, but face-centred cubic structures may not. It is assumed that the interatomic interactions can be represented again by a molecular field, but with a coefficient opposite in sign to that of the Weiss ferromagnetic case. The model is illustrated in Fig. 4.1.

### 4.1.1 *Magnetization of the sublattices*

Let $\sigma_A = \frac{1}{2}N_s \langle \mu_{J\uparrow} \rangle_A$ be the magnetization per unit mass of the A

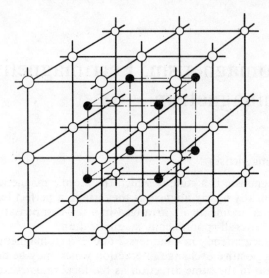

○  A sublattice + spin

●  B sublattice − spin

**Figure 4.1**   Two-sublattice model of an antiferromagnet.

sublattice (half the total number of atoms), and similarly for $\sigma_B$ and the B sublattice.

Taking first- and second-nearest-neighbour interactions into account, the molecular fields acting respectively on the atoms of the A and the B sublattices are

$$B_i^A = q_{AA}\sigma_A + q_{AB}\sigma_B \tag{4.1}$$

and

$$B_i^B = q_{BA}\sigma_A + q_{BB}\sigma_B \tag{4.2}$$

In the present case the two sublattices are equivalent, and

$$q_{AB} = q_{BA} = -q_1 \quad \text{(first neighbours)}$$

and

$$q_{AA} = q_{BB} = -q_2 \quad \text{(second neighbours)}$$

$q_1$ and $q_2$ are both positive.

The magnetizations of the two sublattices may now be written down in a similar way to that for the ferromagnetic case in Chapter 2 (compare equations 2.8 and 2.9). Again we calculate the spontaneous magnetization, with no external field applied:

$$(\sigma_A)_T = \tfrac{1}{2}N_s J g \mu_B F(J, y'_A) \tag{4.3}$$

and

$$(\sigma_B)_T = \tfrac{1}{2}N_s J g \mu_B F(J, y'_B) \tag{4.4}$$

where $y'_A = J g \mu_B B_i^A / kT$, and $y'_B = J g \mu_B B_i^B / kT$. Since $\sigma_A$ and $\sigma_B$ have the same magnitude and opposite directions, we put $\sigma_A = -\sigma_B$ and $|\sigma_A| = \sigma_s$. Then

$$\sigma_s = \tfrac{1}{2}N_s J g \mu_B F(J, y'_s)$$

where $y'_s = J g \mu_B \sigma_s (q_1 - q_2) / kT$. Putting $q_1 - q_2 = q$ (equivalent to $\gamma_m$ in Equ. 2.9) and $\sigma_0 = \tfrac{1}{2}N_s J g \mu_B$ we see that the solution takes exactly the same form as the ferromagnetic case considered in Chapter 2. Each sublattice is expected to be spontaneously magnetized with a value depending on temperature, like Fig. 4.2. The overall magnetization is zero since the two sublattice magnetizations are always equal and opposite.

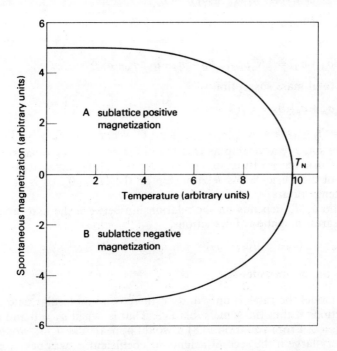

**Figure 4.2**  Spontaneous magnetization of the sublattices in a simple antiferromagnet.

Sublattice magnetizations may be measured by neutron diffraction, from the intensity of the magnetic scattering of the neutrons. Observations made on ionic materials ($MnF_2$ is an example) have confirmed the theory given above to be essentially correct.

The Néel temperature $T_N$ may be calculated as $T_C$ was calculated in the ferromagnetic case, with $\gamma_m$ replaced by $q = q_1 - q_2$:

$$T_N = (q_1 - q_2)\tfrac{1}{2}N_s g^2 \mu_B^2 J(J+1)/3k = \tfrac{1}{2}(q_1 - q_2)\ C \qquad (4.5)$$

### 4.1.2  Susceptibility above the Néel temperature

Here the magnetizations are again small and we can use the approximate form of the Brillouin function. For the magnetizations of the two sublattices

$$\sigma_A = \tfrac{1}{2}N_s p_{eff}^2 (B_0 - q_2\sigma_A - q_1\sigma_B)/3\,kT$$

and

$$\sigma_B = \tfrac{1}{2}N_s p_{eff}^2 (B_0 - q_1\sigma_A - q_2\sigma_B)/3\,kT$$

where, as in Chapter 2, $p_{eff}^2 = g^2 \mu_B^2 J(J+1)$. Adding these two equations together,

$$3\,kT(\sigma_A + \sigma_B) = \tfrac{1}{2}N_s p_{eff}^2 [2B_0 - (q_1 + q_2)(\sigma_A + \sigma_B)] \qquad (4.6)$$

Thus the total mass susceptibility

$$\chi = (\sigma_A + \sigma_B)/B_0 = C/(T - \theta_p) \qquad (4.7)$$

where $C = N_s p_{eff}^2/3k$ and $\theta_p = -\tfrac{1}{2}(q_1 + q_2)\ C$. When $T = T_N$, $\chi = 1/q_1$. This is the same relationship as that found for an ionic ferromagnet above its Curie temperature, except that for the antiferromagnet the intercept of the Curie–Weiss relationship on the $1/\chi = 0$ axis is at a negative temperature.

The ratio $\theta_p/T_N$ depends on the relationship between the first- and the second-nearest-neighbour interactions.

$$\theta_p/T_N = -(q_1 + q_2)/(q_1 - q_2) \qquad (4.8)$$

$\theta_p$ and $T_N$ are of opposite sign

In this model the ratio is only unity if there is no molecular field due to interactions within the same sublattice. That is, when $q_2 = 0$ and also $q_{AA} = q_{BB} = 0$. From equation (4.8) it would appear that $\theta_p/T_N$ would become very large if the second-neighbour coefficient $q_2$ was nearly equal to $q_1$. In fact this is not the case, for if the ratio $q_2/q_1$ exceeds a certain value it is energetically more favourable to have a different magnetic structure in which all the spins in sublattice A cease to be parallel to each other and similarly with sublattice B. A new arrangement of sublattices forms. The sublattice arrangement of a given antiferromagnetic material can generally be found by neutron diffraction experiments.

In general, a given crystal structure may be made up of more than two magnetic sublattices. A face-centred cubic lattice can be regarded as being made up of four simple cubic sublattices. The twelve nearest neighbours of a given atom of any given sublattice are distributed equally among the three other sublattices. The six second-nearest neighbours belong to the same sublattice as the given atom. The treatment is now more complicated but the general results are similar to the two-sublattice case. However, the ratio $\theta_p/T_N$ is differently related to $q_1$ and $q_2$.

### 4.1.3  Susceptibility below the Néel temperature

In calculating the susceptibility below $T_N$ it is important to take into account the direction of the applied field with respect to the direction of the spins. There are major differences according to whether the field and the spins are perpendicular to each other or whether they lie along the same direction. In general, particularly in a polycrystalline material, the relative orientation will be somewhere between these limits. The simplest assumption to make is that the spins of all the various sublattices in one domain all point parallel to or antiparallel to the same direction. This direction will vary from one domain to another. We may take the average of the effects throughout the sample of the perpendicular and the parallel components of the field by writing

$$\chi = \tfrac{2}{3}\chi_\perp + \tfrac{1}{3}\chi_\parallel \tag{4.9}$$

What happens when perpendicular and parallel fields are applied to such an antiferromagnet can be seen qualitatively from Fig. 4.3. In the perpendicular case, application of a field increases the magnetization in the field direction equally for both kinds of spin. Representing the effect of increasing temperature by showing an increasing divergence of spins, we expect the induced magnetization and thus the perpendicular susceptibility to be the same at all temperatures from $T = 0$ to $T = T_N$. In the parallel direction at $T = 0$ we expect a small field to have no effect on the spins and the parallel susceptibility to be zero. When the divergence increases, representing the effect of increasing temperature, there is more out-of-line moment which may be pulled into line by the field. That is,

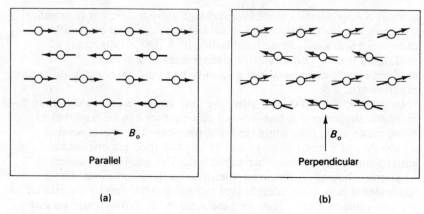

**Figure 4.3** Application of (a) parallel and (b) perpendicular field to a simple antiferromagnet.

we expect a parallel susceptibility which increases from $\chi_{\parallel} = 0$ at $T = 0$ until it reaches the paramagnetic value at $T = T_N$. We would also expect that a very strong field would tend to reverse antiparallel spins and would convert the antiferromagnetic state into one with a nearly saturated ferromagnetic moment.

### 4.1.4 Perpendicular susceptibility

The effect of the field is to deflect the magnetic moments $\sigma_A$ and $\sigma_B$ of both sublattices through a small angle $\theta$ towards the direction of the field (Fig. 4.3b). It is assumed that the magnitudes of $\sigma_A$ and $\sigma_B$ remain unchanged. The angle of deflection $\theta$ is that angle at which the torques from the various fields acting on a given spin balance out to give no overall effect. The A sublattice is acted upon by:

(a) the applied field $B_0$, exerting a torque $B_0 \cos \theta$ which is clockwise in the diagram;

(b) the first-neighbour molecular field $q_1 \sigma_B$, exerting a torque of $q_1 \sigma_B \sin 2\theta$ (anticlockwise); and

(c) the second-neighbour molecular field $q_2 \sigma_A$, exerting no torque since it always has the same direction as $\sigma_A$.

For small $\theta$, in equilibrium

$$B_0 = q_1 \sigma_B 2\theta \quad \text{or} \quad \theta = \tfrac{1}{2} B_0 / \sigma_s q_1$$

The magnetization induced in the direction of the field is $2 \sigma_s \theta$, and the perpendicular susceptibility is given by

$$\chi_{\perp} = 2 \sigma_s \theta / B_0 = 1/q_1 \tag{4.10}$$

This is independent of temperature so long as the first molecular field coefficient $q_1$ is independent of temperature. It is equal to the value of the paramagnetic susceptibility at $T_N$.

### 4.1.5 Parallel susceptibility

In calculating the parallel susceptibility we need to know the changes $\Delta\sigma_A$ and $\Delta\sigma_B$ produced in the magnetization of each sublattice when the field (assumed to be in the direction of $\sigma_A$ and antiparallel to $\sigma_B$) changes from zero to $B_0$. Then

$$\chi_{\parallel} = (\Delta\sigma_A + \Delta\sigma_B)/B_0$$

Again we write (similarly to equations 4.3 and 4.4)

$$\sigma_A = \tfrac{1}{2}N_s J g \mu_B F(J, y''_A) \tag{4.11}$$

and

$$\sigma_B = \tfrac{1}{2}N_s J g \mu_B F(J, y''_B) \tag{4.12}$$

where

$$y''_A = J g \mu_B (B_0 - q_1\sigma_B - q_2\sigma_A)/kT$$
$$-y''_B = J g \mu_B (B_0 - q_1\sigma_A - q_2\sigma_B)/kT$$

and $F(J, y'')$ is the Brillouin function. As an approximation in the expression for $y''$ we write $\sigma_A = -\sigma_B$. Then

$$y''_A = J g \mu_B [\sigma(q_1 - q_2) + B_0]/kT \tag{4.13}$$

and

$$y''_B = J g \mu_B [\sigma(q_1 - q_2) - B_0]/kT \tag{4.14}$$

Equations 4.13 and 4.14 may be written in the form of Equ. 2.10:

$$\sigma_A/J g \mu_B N_s = ATy'' - C \tag{4.15}$$

and

$$\sigma_B/J g \mu_B N_s = ATy'' + C \tag{4.16}$$

where

$$A = k/[(J g \mu_B)^2 N_s(q_1 - q_2)]$$

and

$$C = B_0/[J g \mu_B N_s(q_1 - q_2)]$$

The magnetization $\sigma_A$ of the A sublattice is given by the simultaneous solution of equations 4.11 and 4.15, or equations 4.12 and 4.16 for $\sigma_B$.

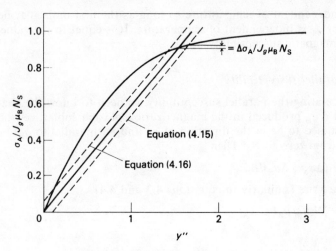

**Figure 4.4**  Solution of equations 4.11 and 4.15.

(Fig. 4.4). $\Delta\sigma_A$ is the change in $\sigma_A$ when $B_0$ is increased from zero, and likewise for $\Delta\sigma_B$.

$\Delta\sigma_A$ is given by $B_0/(q_1 - q_2)$ times the gradient of the Brillouin function evaluated at the equilibrium value of $y''$ when $B_0 = 0$. $\Delta\sigma_B$ has the same value as $\Delta\sigma_A$, since it corresponds to a decrease in magnetization in the direction opposite to that of the field. The parallel susceptibility $\chi_{\parallel} = (\Delta\sigma_A + \Delta\sigma_B)/B_0$ is therefore approximately proportional to the gradient of the Brillouin function against $y''$, evaluated for $B_0 = 0$.

When the sublattice magnetization is saturated (at $T = 0$ and therefore high values of $y''$), $\chi_{\parallel}$ is zero. $\chi_{\parallel}$ rises with increasing temperature until it reaches the value for the paramagnetic state ($y'' \to 0$) at $T = T_N$. Also at the Néel temperature, $\chi_{\parallel} = \chi_{\perp}$. The susceptibility of a randomly oriented polycrystalline sample is now

$$\chi = \tfrac{2}{3}\chi_{\perp} + \tfrac{1}{3}\chi_{\parallel} \tag{4.17}$$

The expected variation with temperature of the susceptibility of an ionic antiferromagnet is shown in Fig. 4.5. We have been discussing a model in which the ions may be distributed between two magnetic sublattices. The numerical details of the calculation are different for more sublattices but the principal feature of the result, the expected maximum of the susceptibility at $T_N$, remains. This is usually found experimentally for ionic antiferromagnets, as Fig. 4.6 illustrates.

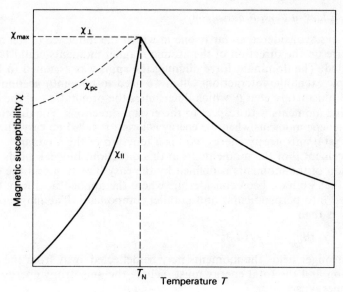

**Figure 4.5** Calculated susceptibility of a simple ionic antiferromagnetic single crystal respectively parallel and perpendicular to the moment axis, and for a polycrystalline powder. (After Schieber, 1967, *Experimental Magnetochemistry*, North Holland, p. 47.)

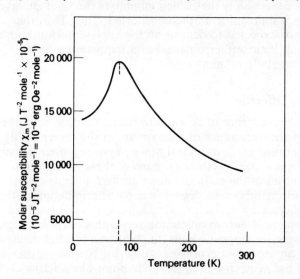

**Figure 4.6** Measured susceptibility of antiferromagnetic $FeF_2$. The Néel temperature $T_N$ is 79 K. (After Bizette, 1951, *J. Physique*, **12,** 161.)

### 4.1.6    *Effect of crystal anisotropy*

The case considered so far is one in which the influence of the crystal structure on the direction of the atomic magnet moments could be neglected. The dominant force aligning the spins was assumed to be the isotropic exchange interaction. Often we need to take into account a crystal anisotropy energy which determines the orientation of the magnetic moments with respect to the crystal directions. The direction of the magnetic moments when the energy is lowest is called an easy direction. The crystal anisotropy energy $\Phi(\theta)$ is a function of the angular displacement $\theta$ of the moments from this direction. In weak fields the direction of the moments is defined by the easy direction and the case holds that we have been considering, where the applied field may be resolved into perpendicular and parallel components. The magnetic energy is then

$$-\tfrac{1}{2}\chi_\perp (B_0)_\perp^2 - \tfrac{1}{2}\chi_\| (B_0)_\|^2$$

In stronger fields the moments may be deflected away from the easy direction and the total energy must include the anisotropy energy. The total energy is

$$E = -\tfrac{1}{2}\chi_\perp (B_0)_\perp^2 - \tfrac{1}{2}\chi_\| (B_0)_\|^2 + \Phi(\theta) \tag{4.18}$$

The angle of deflection is that which minimizes the total energy, and the susceptibility is different from the undeflected value. Thus the susceptibility is expected to depend on the applied field at high field strengths in an ionic antiferromagnet at a temperature below $T_N$. This is found experimentally in many cases.


## 4.2    Neutron diffraction

The probable existence of an antiferromagnetic state may often be inferred from the occurrence of a maximum in the susceptibility. Irregularities occur at $T_N$ in several other physical properties, such as in the specific heat capacity. However, none of these observations gives a certain indication of the existence of an antiferromagnetic state. The only certain way of unambiguous detection is by determination of the magnetic structure by diffraction of radiation which is sensitive to the magnetic moment. Neutron diffraction serves this purpose uniquely. The neutron possesses a magnetic moment. When an incident neutron is scattered by an atom two processes can occur. Nuclear scattering is scattering of the neutron by the relatively point-like nucleus of the scatterer. Magnetic scattering is scattering by the electronic magnetic moment located at a significant radial distance out from the nucleus of the scattering atom. Its magnitude is a measure of the magnetic moment of the scattering point. Both kinds of scattering take place at the same time.

The wave nature of the neutron is well known. The wavelength is given by $\lambda = h/mv$, where $h$ is Planck's constant, $m$ is the mass of the neutron, $v$ is the velocity of the neutron.

Beams of neutrons for diffraction purposes are usually obtained from nuclear fission reactors. In the reactor the neutrons undergo numerous collisions with atoms of the moderator and they achieve an equilibrium mean thermal energy appropriate to the temperature of the moderator. This dictates the mean velocity and thus the mean wavelength of the neutrons. When the temperature of the moderator is about 320 K the mean wavelength is about 1·4 Å (1 Å = $10^{-10}$ m). This wavelength is of the same order as interatomic distances in crystals. Thermal neutrons are therefore useful in investigating the crystal structures of solids. In practice a monochromating crystal is employed whereby only those neutrons of fixed wavelength that are scattered at a selected angle by the monochromator are allowed to fall on the specimen under investigation. The experimental arrangement is similar to that of an X-ray diffractometer. A collimated monochromatic beam of neutrons is incident on the specimen. One or more neutron counters can then be tracked round the specimen to measure the angular dependence of the scattered neutron intensity. Either powder or single-crystal instruments are available. Experiments can be made with polarized neutrons, although that aspect is not considered here. Also, we are concerned here only with the elastic scattering of neutrons, when the incident and scattered wavelengths are the same.

If the atoms of the sample have no magnetic moments only nuclear scattering contributes to the diffraction pattern. The criteria for the positions of the lines in the powder diffraction pattern are the same as for X-rays. If $\theta$ is the Bragg diffraction angle

$$\sin \theta = (\lambda/2) |G| \tag{4.19}$$

$\lambda$ is the wavelength and $|G|$ is the magnitude of a reciprocal lattice vector. For a structure with a rectilinear unit cell

$$|G| = (h^2/a^2 + k^2/b^2 + l^2/c^2)^{\frac{1}{2}} \tag{4.20}$$

The X-ray and neutron scattering amplitudes of atoms are not related to each other and the relative intensities of different lines in a powder pattern will in general differ between X-ray and neutron diffraction.

With magnetic scattering there may be major differences. If in an antiferromagnet alternate atoms along a particular crystallographic direction have magnetic moments pointing oppositely, the crystallographic repeat distance that the magnetic moment of the neutrons see will be doubled. The magnetic unit cell will be larger than the chemical crystallographic cell and in general the magnetic diffraction lines will have different positions from those of the nuclear lines. It is common practice when dealing with magnetic scattering to refer to the chemical cell and to employ fractional indices where appropriate for magnetic reflections. In a cubic crystal having atomic magnetic moments alternating along a 1 1 0 (face diagonal) direction, the relevant magnetic line would be indexed $\frac{1}{2}$ $\frac{1}{2}$ 0. The neutron diffraction patterns and structure of a typical antiferromagnet are shown in Figs. 4.7 and 4.8.

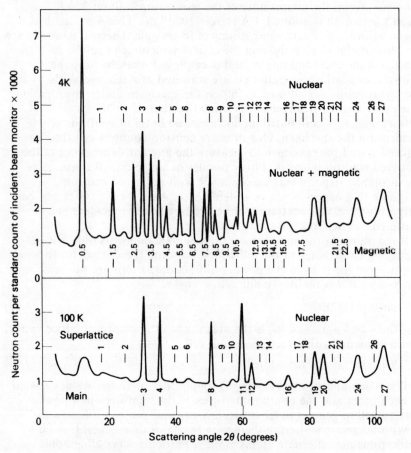

**Figure 4.7**   Neutron diffraction pattern of TbIn₃.

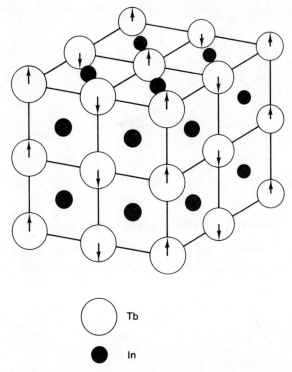

**Figure 4.8**  Crystal and magnetic structures of TbIn$_3$.

It is generally possible to determine the layout of the magnetic unit cell from neutron diffraction experiments and to measure the magnetic moments of the atoms concerned, although the experimental errors are sometimes relatively large. However, it is not always possible to find unambiguously the direction in which the moments point within the crystal.

## 4.3  Antiferromagnetism in metals

The antiferromagnetic properties described so far relate most closely to non-metals. The ions are well-separated and we are not much concerned with band properties. Many metals also are antiferromagnetic but their properties tend to be complicated by the effects of energy bands of appreciable width and the effects of conduction electrons. There is a wide variety of behaviour. Some metals have simple antiferromagnetic structures and their susceptibilities follow the Curie–Weiss law above $T_N$

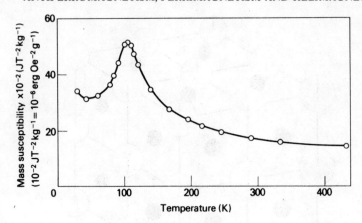

**Figure 4.9**   Susceptibility of metallic antiferromagnetic $Pt_3Fe$.

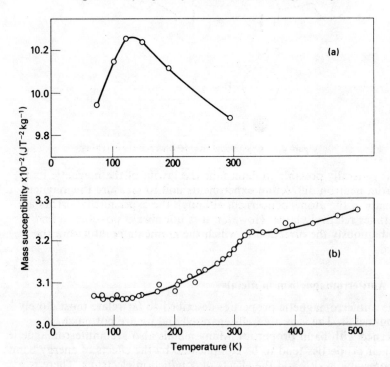

**Figure 4.10**   (a) Susceptibility of α-manganese. (After Kriessman and McGuire, 1955, *Phys. Rev.*, **98**, 936.) (b) Susceptibility of chromium. (After Lingelbach, 1958, *Z. Phys. Chem.*, **14**, 1.)

with a clear maximum at the Néel temperature. An example is given in Fig. 4.9. Sometimes metals are antiferromagnetic and little if any effect on the susceptibility is seen at $T_N$. Metallic manganese and chromium are examples of this (Fig. 4.10). The simple ionic theory of the susceptibility cannot usually be applied to metallic antiferromagnets. Other more complicated forms of antiferromagnetism occur which involve non-collinear moments. Some of these are described later in this chapter.

## 4.4  Ferrimagnetism

A ferrimagnetic material is one in which the magnetic moments of the atoms on different sublattices oppose as in antiferromagnets; but the opposing moments are unequal and a spontaneous magnetization remains. This behaviour was first recognized in the technologically important group of materials called ferrites.

### 4.4.1  *Structure of the spinel ferrites*

These ferrites are semiconductors having the general chemical formula $X\,O.Y_2O_3$, the $X$ cation usually being divalent and the $Y$ cation trivalent. These substances possess the so-called spinel structure. This consists of a close-packed face-centred cubic arrangement of the oxygen anions, the cations being distributed in the interstitial sites between them. The unit cell is illustrated in Fig. 4.11. It contains 32 anions and altogether 24

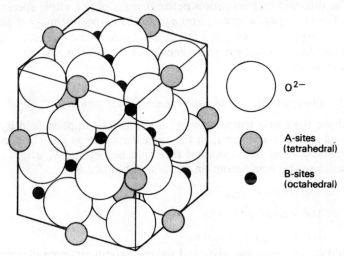

**Figure 4.11**   Crystal structure of a normal spinel.

cations of both kinds. Eight cations on A sites are surrounded tetrahedrally by four oxygen ions and the remaining sixteen cations on B sites are surrounded octahedrally by six oxygen ions. In the structure which is called normal the divalent $X$ cations occupy the tetrahedral A sites and the trivalent $Y$ ions occupy the octahedral B sites. The structure called inverse occurs when half the $Y$ ions occupy A sites, the remaining $X$ and $Y$ cations being randomly distributed among the octahedral B sites. These structures were found by diffraction methods. Some ferrites, such as magnesium ferrite $MgO.Fe_2O_3$, possess the inverse structure and some, such as zinc ferrite $ZnO.Fe_2O_3$ have the normal structure.

The general properties of spinel ferrites were explained by Néel's (1948) two-sublattice theory of (collinear) ferrimagnetism.

Other materials in the same general class are the hexagonal ferrites (magnetoplumbites) such as barium ferrite $BaFe_{12}O_{19}$; and the ferrimagnetic garnets. A well-known example of the latter is yttrium iron garnet. This is also called YIG, $Y_3Fe_5O_{12}$ or $5\ Fe_2O_3.3\ Y_2O_3$.

### 4.4.2   *Two-sublattice theory of ferrimagnetism*

The two-sublattice theory of ferrimagnetism first given by Néel (1948) is really an extension of the one described already for a two-sublattice antiferromagnet. The magnetizations of the two sublattices oppose each other but they are not equal.

The intrinsic magnetization per unit mass of the whole specimen is $\sigma = \lambda \sigma_1 - (1-\lambda)\sigma_2$, where $\sigma_1$ and $\sigma_2$ are the respective magnetizations of the two sublattices and $\lambda$ is a fraction between 0 and 1. When $\lambda = \frac{1}{2}$ we have antiferromagnetism and when $\lambda = 1$ (or zero) we have ferromagnetism.

### 4.4.3   *Susceptibility of the paramagnetic state above $T_C$*

Above the Curie temperature $y''$ is small. The applied field $B_0$ induces a small moment $\sigma$ which is in the same direction as $B_0$. The sublattice magnetization $\sigma_1$ is in the same direction but $\sigma_2$ and $B_0$ are in opposite directions. The field acting on the first sublattice is

$$B_0 + q_1(1-\lambda)\sigma_2 + q_2 \lambda \sigma_1$$

and on the second sublattice

$$-B_0 + q_1 \lambda \sigma_1 + q_2(1-\lambda)\sigma_2$$

$q_1$ and $q_2$ are again the first- and second neighbour molecular field coefficients. We allow for the possibility of the two sublattices being made up of different kinds of ion (with different $p_{eff}$), and in the approximate form of the Brillouin function we write $C = N_s p_{eff}^2/3k$, so that

$$\sigma_1 = [B_0 + q_1(1 - \lambda)\sigma_2 + q_2\lambda\sigma_1]C_1/T \tag{4.21}$$

and

$$\sigma_2 = [-B_0 + q_1\lambda\sigma_1 + q_2(1 - \lambda)\sigma_2]C_2/T \tag{4.22}$$

These equations may be solved for $\sigma_1$ and $\sigma_2$ and the reciprocal of the total susceptibility is

$$1/\chi = B_0/\sigma = B_0/[\lambda\sigma_1 - (1 - \lambda)\sigma_2]$$

The solution may be written in the form

$$1/\chi = T/C + 1/\chi_0 + A/(T - \theta) \tag{4.23}$$

where $C, \chi_0, A$ and $\theta$ are constants which may be expressed in terms of $\lambda$, $q_1, q_2, C_1$ and $C_2$.

This relationship shows a hyperbolic dependence of $1/\chi$ on $T$, agreeing with what is often found experimentally in ferrimagnets (Fig. 1.11). It approaches a Curie–Weiss relationship at high temperatures, when the term $A/(T - \theta)$ becomes small.

The Curie temperature $T_C$, the highest temperature at which a spontaneous magnetic moment can exist, may be calculated in this theory by writing $1/\chi = 0$ and $T = T_C$ in Eq. 4.23.

### 4.4.4   Magnetization below the Curie temperature

Néel applied the two-sublattice theory to calculate the magnetization of each sublattice below $T_C$, and therefore total magnetization. Instead of using the approximate form of the Brillouin function in the expressions for $\sigma_1$ and $\sigma_2$ (equations 4.21 and 4.22) the full form was used. A numerical method of solution for $\sigma_1$ and $\sigma_2$ was followed, very similar to that described in Section 2.5.1 for the single-sublattice ionic ferromagnet.

The way in which total spontaneous magnetization $\sigma = \lambda\sigma_1 - (1 - \lambda)\sigma_2$ of the ferrimagnet varies with temperature depends markedly on the relative magnitudes of the molecular field coefficients and of the quantity parameter $\lambda$. Some of the kinds of result which Néel predicted are shown qualitatively in Fig. 4.12. All these forms of curve have now been observed experimentally, supporting Néel's theory in a remarkable way. Fig. 4.13 shows the experimentally determined curve of spontaneous magnetization against temperature for manganese ferrite.

The unusual result, that in some cases the net magnetic moment

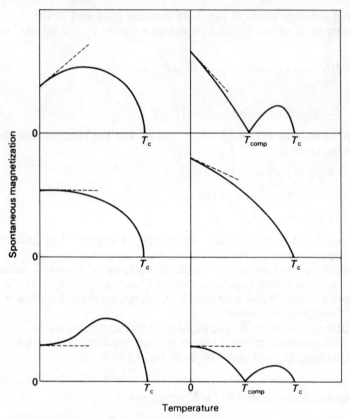

**Figure 4.12** Predicted curves of magnetization against temperature for two-sublattice ferrimagnets. (After Néel, 1948, *Ann. Phys., Lpz.,* 154.)

changes its sign and goes through a so-called compensation point of zero value before finally vanishing at the Curie temperature, is illustrated from experiment in Fig. 4.14. In most measurements the question of which sublattice dominates is not obvious. Between the compensation temperature and $T_C$ the spontaneous magnetization appears to increase with increasing temperature, pass through a maximum and then finally approach zero again at $T_C$.

### 4.4.5  *Saturation magnetic moment of spinel ferrites*

When it is known which magnetic ions occupy which kind of site within the crystal structure the saturation moment may be calculated

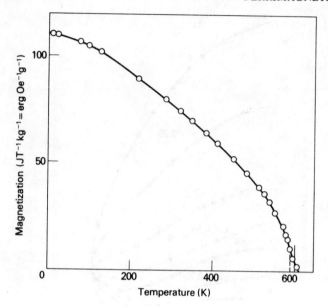

**Figure 4.13** Experimental graph of magnetization against temperature for manganese ferrite $MnO.Fe_2O_3$.

very simply. In some cases the structure lies between inverse and normal, the occupation parameters for the A and B sites being known from neutron diffraction experiments. Characteristics of several kinds of cation are given in Table 4.1. Calculated and experimental values of the saturation magnetic moments of a number of spinel ferrites are given in Table 4.2. There is generally quite good agreement between experiment and theory.

Zinc ferrite $ZnO.Fe_2O_3$ has the normal structure and $Zn^{2+}$ ions have a strong preference for A sites. If mixed ferrites are prepared in which $Zn^{2+}$ ions replace other divalent ions in an inverse ferrite, for example $Co^{2+}$, $Fe^{3+}$ ions are displaced to the B sites. The B site moment is therefore increased, unless its value is already the maximum of $(5+5)\,\mu_B = 10\,\mu_B$, and the opposing A site moment is decreased by dilution by the non-magnetic $Zn^{2+}$ ions. Thus we have the unusual situation that dilution by a non-magnetic material increases the magnetic moment. The initial rate of rise of moment is such that extrapolation to fully substituted $ZnO.Fe_2O_3$ (Fig. 4.15) leads to an expected moment of $10\,\mu_B$ per molecular unit. However, other factors come into play and pure zinc ferrite is non-magnetic.

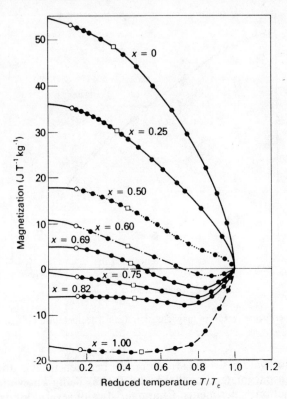

**Figure 4.14** Spontaneous magnetization plotted against temperature for the compensation point system $Ni\ Fe_{2-x}\ V_x\ O_4$. (After Blasse and Gorter, 1962, *J. Phys. Soc. Japan*, **17**(B1), 176.)

In addition to the collinear ferrimagnetic structure described here, a so-called triangular structure can occur. The total energy is lower in these cases when some of the ionic magnetizations make an angle with each other that differs from 0° or 180°. Yafet and Kittel suggested that, where the A–A and B–B interactions are not small compared with A–B, the A and the B sublattices can be split further into $A_1$ and $A_2$, $B_1$ and $B_2$. Non-collinear angles occur between the magnetization vectors within A and B but the resultant magnetizations of A and B are still antiparallel.

### 4.4.6  *Hexagonal ferrites*

One range of ferrimagnetic oxides has the same hexagonal crystal structure as the mineral magnetoplumbite $PbFe_{12}O_{19}$. Most of these compounds are ferrimagnetic but some are antiferromagnetic. Barium ferrite $BaFe_{12}O_{19}$ is one of them which has been studied extensively. Its most important use is as a material for permanent magnets and it is known commercially as Ferroxdure. The ferrimagnetic members of this group of compounds have Curie temperatures between 500 K and 800 K. Their magnetic moments can be explained by the simple Néel model of ferrimagnetism in terms of the known occupation of the various lattice sites in the structure. The usefulness of barium ferrite for making permanent magnets lies in it having strong magnetic anisotropy with a preference for the magnetic moment to lie along the hexagonal $c$-axis. The coercivity is of the order of 0·3 T (3000 Oe). In a few of the other ferrites of this general kind the anisotropy is predominant within the basal plane of the hexagonal structure. These are called by the commercial name Ferroxplane.

**Table 4.1**  Characteristics of cations in spinel ferrites.

| Cation | Number of 3d-electrons | Spin-only magnetic moment ($\mu_B$) |
|---|---|---|
| $Sc^{3+}$ | 0 | 0 |
| $Ti^{3+}$ | 1 | 1 |
| $Ti^{2+}$ $V^{3+}$ | 2 | 2 |
| $V^{2+}$ $Cr^{3+}$ | 3 | 3 |
| $Cr^{2+}$ $Mn^{3+}$ | 4 | 4 |
| $Mn^{2+}$ $Fe^{3+}$ | 5 | 5 |
| $Fe^{2+}$ $Co^{3+}$ | 6 | 4 |
| $Co^{2+}$ $Ni^{3+}$ | 7 | 3 |
| $Ni^{2+}$ | 8 | 2 |
| $Cu^{2+}$ | 9 | 1 |
| $Cu^{+}$ $Zn^{2+}$ | 10 | 0 |

**Table 4.2**  Calculated and Experimental Saturation Magnetic Moments in Spinel Ferrites.

| Material | Ion distribution | | Sublattice moment | | Saturation moment | |
|---|---|---|---|---|---|---|
| | A sites | B sites | A sites | B sites | Calculated | Experimental |
| $MnOFe_2O_3$ | $Fe_{0.2}^{3+} Mn_{0.8}^{2+}$ | $Mn_{0.2}^{2+} Fe_{1.8}^{3+}$ | 5 | 5+5 | 5 | 4·6 |
| $FeOFe_2O_3$ | $Fe^{3+}$ | $Fe^{2+} Fe^{3+}$ | 5 | 4+5 | 4 | 4·1 |
| $CoOFe_2O_3$ | $Fe^{3+}$ | $Co^{2+} Fe^{3+}$ | 5 | 3+5 | 3 | 3·7 |
| $NiOFe_2O_3$ | $Fe^{3+}$ | $Ni^{2+} Fe^{3+}$ | 5 | 2+5 | 2 | 2·3 |
| $CuOFe_2O_3$ | $Fe^{3+}$ | $Cu^{2+} Fe^{3+}$ | 5 | 1+5 | 1 | 1·3 |
| $MgOFe_2O_3$ | $Fe^{3+}$ | $Mg^{+} Fe^{3+}$ | 5 | 0+5 | 0 | 1·1 |

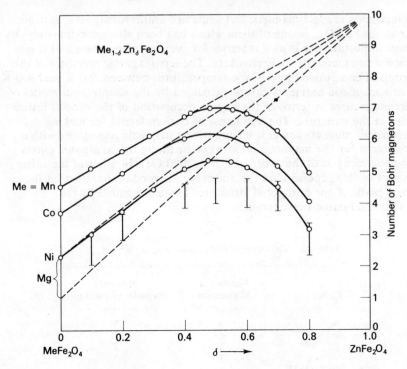

**Figure 4.15** Saturation magnetic moment of various ferrites diluted with zinc ferrite. (After Guillaud, 1951, *J. Physique*, **12**, 239.)

### 4.4.7 Ferrimagnetic garnets

This is another range of ferrimagnetic oxides having important applications. Their general formula is $R_3Fe_5O_{12}$, where $R$ is a rare-earth ion or yttrium. Yttrium is not strictly a rare earth but its chemical behaviour is like one and it is often loosely regarded as a rare earth.

The garnets have a complicated cubic crystal structure, with eight formula units per unit cell. The rare-earth iron garnets are ferrimagnetic with Curie temperatures of about 550 K. The general formula can be represented by

$$\{C_3\}[A_2](D_3)O_{12}$$

where the cations are subdivided into three main sites with different crystallographic coordinations. In this representation yttrium iron garnet $Y_3Fe_5O_{12}$ becomes $\{Y_3\}[Fe_2](Fe_3)O_{12}$.

The cation $C$ has the dodecahedral coordination and occupies the $c$ crystallographic positions, of which there are 24: that is, $\{24c\}$.

The cation $A$ has octahedral coordination and occupies the $[16a]$ positions.

The cation $D$ has tetrahedral coordination and occupies $(24d)$ positions.

Which cations can occupy these sites is determined by their relative sizes. In general the rare-earth ions go into $\{24c\}$ sites.

The ferrimagnetic properties can be interpreted on the basis of a collinear model. The distribution of magnetic moments is written as $R\uparrow/\downarrow_3$ $Fe\uparrow_2$ $Fe\downarrow_3$ $O_{12}$. The $[a]$ and the $(d)$ $Fe^{3+}$ sublattices are antiparallel, their difference being one $Fe^{3+}$ ion, or a moment of 5 $\mu_B$ per formula unit. The $R$ moment on $\{c\}$ sites can be either parallel or antiparallel to the net iron moment, depending on the identity of $R$.

### 4.4.8  Applications of ferrimagnetic oxides

The technical applications of oxide ferrimagnets are largely related to the coexistence of their relatively large magnetization and their properties as insulators. An important use of magnetically soft spinel ferrites is for making cores for high-frequency transformers and inductors. Low anisotropy garnet-type ferrites are used in various devices operating at microwave frequencies. Hexagonal ferrites are widely used as permanent magnets, often in high-frequency applications.

### 4.4.9  Mechanism of magnetic coupling in ferrimagnetic oxides

The source of the magnetic coupling in magnetic insulators is usually the process called superexchange. A non-magnetic anion such as oxygen takes part in a magnetic bond. A central anion interacts simultaneously with neighbouring magnetic cations and interposes a correlation between their directions of magnetization. The mechanism is described in more detail in Chapter 5.

## 4.5  Helimagnetism

So far we have dealt mostly with simple collinear magnetic systems in which all the atomic magnetic moments in a domain lie parallel to or antiparallel to a single direction. These are common but special cases of a more general situation in which non-collinear arrangements occur.

The first material in which such behaviour was found was the intermetallic compound $MnAu_2$. This is one of a series of such compounds formed at different stoichiometries across the

D

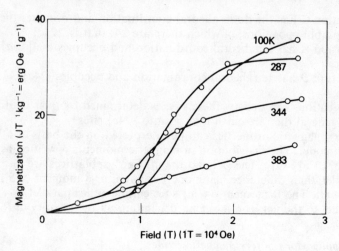

**Figure 4.16** Variation of magnetization of MnAu$_2$ with field at different temperatures, showing metamagnetic behaviour. (After Meyer and Taglang, 1956, *J. Physique*, **17**, 457.)

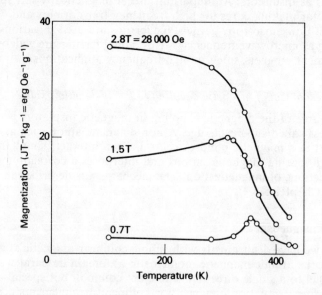

**Figure 4.17** Graphs of magnetization against temperature for MnAu$_2$ measured in different field strengths, showing the effect of breakdown of the magnetic spiral. (After Meyer and Taglang 1956, *J. Physique*, **17**, 457.)

gold–manganese alloy system. In weak applied fields the compound is apparently antiferromagnetic with a Néel temperature of 365 K. Under the influence of strong fields at temperatures below $T_N$ it undergoes a transition to a quasi-ferromagnetic state. This kind of behaviour is known as metamagnetism and it is illustrated in Figs. 4.16 and 4.17.

Observations by neutron diffraction led to a clearer understanding of the magnetic properties. The neutron diffraction pattern obtained from a powdered sample at a temperature well above $T_N$ was consistent with coherent scattering by the Mn and Au nuclei alone, in their known (from X-ray diffraction) positions within the unit cell. The crystal structure consists of a body-centred tetragonal arrangement of Mn atoms for which $c/a = 2\cdot6$. Each Mn atom has two Au atoms near it, at a fixed distance above and below in the $c$ direction. Thus the manganese atoms are in layers perpendicular to the $c$ axis, the interlayer distance being $c/2$.

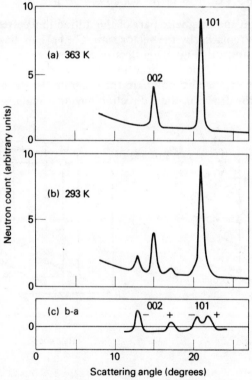

**Figure 4.18** Neutron diffraction patterns of $MnAu_2$, showing evidence of the magnetic spiral (helix). (After Herpin and Meriel 1961, *J. Physique*, **22**, 337.)

At temperatures below $T_N$ extra reflections of magnetic origin were present in the neutron diffraction pattern, occurring in pairs on either side of the respective nuclear reflections (Fig. 4.18). Their positions and intensities were found to be consistent with a spiral arrangement of magnetic moments on the Mn atoms. The screw axis is along the $c$ direction and the moments were found (at room temperature) to change their direction by 102° for each repeat of the unit cell in the $c$ direction, or 51° per layer of Mn atoms. The reasoning was as follows.

The normal condition for diffraction is

$$\sin \theta = (\lambda/2)|G| \qquad (4.19)$$

where $|G|$ is the magnitude of the reciprocal lattice vector $G = h\alpha + k\beta + l\gamma$. $\alpha, \beta$ and $\gamma$ are the primitive translation vectors of the unit cell in reciprocal space. For a structure with a rectilinear unit cell,

$$|G| = (G_x{}^2 + G_y{}^2 + G_z{}^2)^{\frac{1}{2}} = (h^2/a^2 + k^2/b^2 + l^2/c^2)^{\frac{1}{2}} \qquad (4.24)$$

It was found that the magnetic part of the diffraction pattern could be explained if $G$ was replaced by the vector sum $(G \pm v)$. The diagram in reciprocal space shown in Fig. 4.19a illustrates what occurs. The scattering vector $|G + v|$ is the line drawn (in three dimensions) from the origin (0,0,0) to the respective points in the diagram. In the case of MnAu$_2$ $v$ is a vector drawn in the $c$ direction having a magnitude of

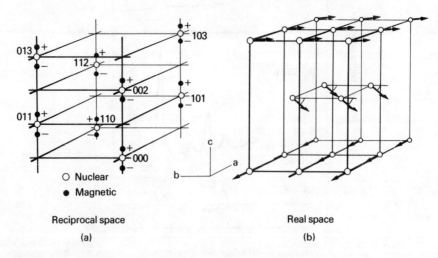

O Nuclear
● Magnetic

Reciprocal space          Real space

(a)                       (b)

**Figure 4.19**    Magnetic structure of MnAu$_2$ at low temperatures: (a) in reciprocal space; and (b) in real space.

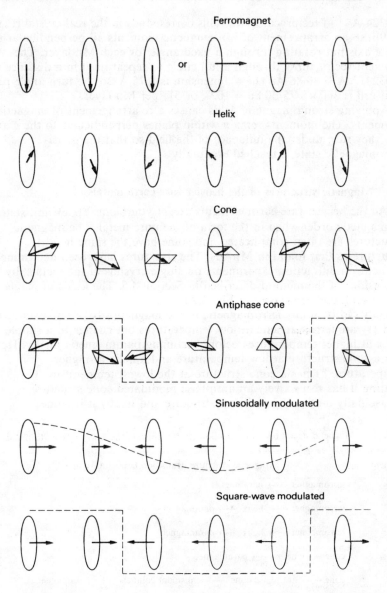

**Figure 4.20** Variety of magnetic structures found in the metallic heavy rare earths.

$0 \cdot 0324$ Å$^{-1}$ in reciprocal space. This corresponds in the real crystal (Fig. 4.19b) to an arrangement of Mn magnetic moments all perpendicular to the $c$ axis but rotating through a fixed angle for each Mn layer. The moment vector turns through a full circle to repeat itself in a distance of $0 \cdot 0324^{-1}$ Å $= 30 \cdot 86$ Å. The $c$ dimension is $8 \cdot 75$ Å, so the turn angle per unit cell is $360 \times 8 \cdot 75/30 \cdot 86 = 102°$, or $51°$ per Mn layer.

Applying strong magnetic fields causes a re-arrangement of magnetic moments. The moments remain within planes perpendicular to the $c$ axis but they turn under the influence of the field so that the quasi-ferromagnetic state is reached eventually.

### 4.6  Magnetic structures of the heavier rare-earth metals

All the heavier rare-earth elements except ytterbium, Yb, exhibit states of magnetic order when in the form of the pure metal. The magnetic structures are often complicated and some have the same helical structure as that found in MnAu$_2$. The structures have been determined by neutron diffraction experiments on single crystals of the metals, by extensions of the method described in Section 4.5. The kinds of magnetic structure found are shown in Fig. 4.20.

Only Gd is simply ferromagnetic in the magnetically ordered state. Tb and Dy are ferromagnetic at low temperatures but change to a simple helix at higher temperatures before becoming paramagnetic finally. Ho has a cone structure at low temperature and a helix at higher temperature. Er has a cone structure at the lowest temperature. On heating it has respectively an antiphase modulated cone structure, a sinusoidally modulated collinear structure and finally it becomes

**Table 4.3**  Magnetic structures and transition temperatures of the heavy rare-earth metals.

| Element | Magnetic structure (transition temperature in K) |
|---|---|
| Gd | ferromagnet $\xrightarrow[293]{}$ paramagnet |
| Tb | ferromagnet $\xrightarrow[220]{}$ helix $\xrightarrow[230]{}$ paramagnet |
| Dy | ferromagnet $\xrightarrow[85]{}$ helix $\xrightarrow[179]{}$ paramagnet |
| Ho | cone $\xrightarrow[20]{}$ helix $\xrightarrow[132]{}$ paramagnet |
| Er | cone $\xrightarrow[20]{}$ antiphase cone $\xrightarrow[53]{}$ sinusoidal collinear $\xrightarrow[85]{}$ paramagnet |
| Tm | square-wave collinear $\xrightarrow[\sim 35]{}$ sinusoidal collinear $\xrightarrow[58]{}$ paramagnet |
| Yb | paramagnet |

paramagnetic. Tm has a square-wave modulated collinear structure at the lowest temperatures, becoming sinusoidally modulated collinear and then paramagnetic. The structures and transition temperatures are summarized in Table 4.3.

The kind of exchange interaction giving rise to helical and other periodically modulated structures are discussed in Chapter 5.

The lighter rare-earth metals, from Ce to Eu, possess more complicated magnetic structures than the heavier ones and some of them are not yet completely understood.

# 5
# Magnetic Interactions and Hyperfine Fields

## 5.1 Exchange interactions in magnetism

So far we have discussed the effects of ferromagnetic and antiferromagnetic order in solids in terms of molecular fields, without attempting to explain the origins of the molecular fields. Dipole–dipole magnetic interactions between local magnetic moments are far too weak to explain the effects observed. Curie temperatures $T_C$ are often of the order of hundreds of kelvins, so that a thermal energy of $kT_C$ $\simeq 10^{-7}$ J per atom is necessary to destroy the magnetically ordered state. The dipole interaction energy is of the order of $\mu_B{}^2/a^3$, about $10^{-9}$ J per atom since the interatomic separation $a$ is about 1 Å. The dipole interactions can therefore be at the most only a correction to the primary effect.

### 5.1.1 *Heisenberg direct exchange between moments localized on atoms*

The idea of exchange coupling between the spins of two or more atoms first appeared clearly in the work of Heitler and London (1927) on chemical binding. It was applied by Heisenberg (1928) to the theory of ferromagnetism. This gave the first explanation of an interaction energy of the correct order of magnitude. It is essentially an electrostatic effect. The relative directions of two interacting spins for quantum mechanical reasons cannot be changed without changing the spatial distribution of charge. The resulting changes in the Coulomb electrostatic energy of the whole system act as though there is a direct coupling between the directions of the spins involved.

We may consider the lobes of charge density corresponding to different electron states in a single free atom and what happens when two such atoms are near to each other. There is a tendency to form overlap regions of charge density contributed to both atoms and the Pauli exclusion principle must be applied to the region of overlap. No single electron state may be occupied twice. When the orbital wavefunction is symmetrical the spin one must be antisymmetrical and *vice versa*.

Changing the spin symmetry by the reversal of one spin must change the orbital symmetry and this redistributes charge. This imposes a correlation between the electron spins of the two atoms. The effect is as though there were an interaction energy between the spin vectors proportional to their scalar product $S_1.S_2$. When the Schrödinger equation of the system is written there is a Heisenberg contribution to the total Hamiltonian

$$\mathcal{H}_{\text{Heis}} = -2J_{12}S_1.S_2 \tag{5.1}$$

This case of two neighbouring atoms is that of the hydrogen molecule and its properties are well known. An embryonic molecular sort of ferromagnetism would occur if the exchange constant $J_{12}$ was positive. This is a 'triplet state', with magnetic quantum numbers $M$ of $-1$, 0 and $+1$. A 'molecular antiferromagnet' occurs for negative $J_{12}$. This is a 'singlet state' having only the magnetic quantum number $M = 0$. For the hydrogen molecule $J_{12}$ is always negative, for all values of the distance of separation between the constituent atoms (Fig. 5.1). Here the triplet state would have an energy greater than that of the two separate atoms and is therefore not favoured†.

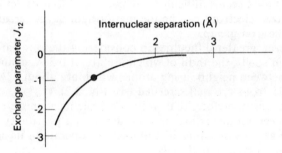

**Figure 5.1**  Exchange interaction parameter of the hydrogen molecule as a function of the internuclear separation of the two atoms. The equilibrium separation is marked.

In an actual solid in which a given atom is surrounded by many others it is necessary to sum the effect of the exchange over all the interactions which can contribute. The Heisenberg Hamiltonian becomes

$$\mathcal{H}_{\text{Heis}} = -2\sum_{i,j}J_{ij}S_i.S_j \tag{5.2}$$

Mostly we are concerned only with interaction between neighbours, and the part of the Hamiltonian that concerns us is

†Coles and Caplin in their book in this series discuss the case of the $O_2$ molecule where parallel spin coupling does have a lower energy.

$$\mathcal{H}' = -2J \sum_{\text{neighbours}} S_i \cdot S_j \qquad (5.3)$$

$J$ is the exchange integral between adjacent atoms and the summation extends over all neighbouring pairs of atoms. Closed shells of electrons contribute nothing to this equation. Exchange effects between electrons of the same atom merely give an additive constant to the energy of the whole system.

In principle the exchange integral can have either sign. A positive value for $J$ leads to ferromagnetism and a negative value leads to antiferromagnetism or ferrimagnetism. However, this statement has really only the status of being a plausible postulate. No rigorous theoretical treatment has yet shown why $J$ should have both the correct sign and the correct magnitude to explain the known ferromagnetic properties of common ferromagnets such as iron, nickel and cobalt. The question remains of why $J$ should be positive in iron when it is definitely negative in the much simpler case of the hydrogen molecule. In fact the most recent and reliable calculations, published by Watson, Freeman and Nesbet in 1962, find $J$ to be about two orders of magnitude too small to account for the measured Curie temperature of nickel and to have the wrong sign. Thus it seems difficult to be convinced that direct exchange between localized electrons can be the main origin of the ferromagnetism in metals of the iron group.

There are even greater difficulties in considering the rare-earth metals. The 4f-electron shells, the radii of which are about 0·3 Å, cannot overlap significantly between neighbouring atoms, which are about 3 Å apart. Also, the 4f-electrons are well screened (see Fig. 2.7).

It would appear, therefore, that while the basic mechanism of direct exchange between moments localized on atoms is a possibility for magnetic interactions in solids, it is unlikely to operate in its simplest form except in a very few materials.

### 5.1.2 *Exchange effects between collective electrons*

So far in this chapter we have been considering exchange between localized magnetic moments. This model can have little relevance to magnetic interactions between electrons described by bands and moving relatively freely throughout a metal.

There is still considerable doubt about how the exchange energy arises in metals in which the ferromagnetism is due to electrons in a partly filled band of strongly 3d-like character. Different authors have expressed apparently equally valid diverging opinions.

One point of view is as follows. Various factors operate which tend to keep electrons apart. One of them is ordinary Coulomb repulsion between like charges. These are called correlation effects. The correlation energy for 3d-band electrons is difficult to estimate and it is of uncertain magnitude. This view assumes that the correlation energy is not large enough to prevent magnetic carriers (either electrons or electron holes) from coming together on the same atom. The origin of the ferromagnetism would then be the kind of intra-atomic exchange coupling that is responsible for Hund's rules and dominates the arrangement of electrons in atoms. This provides a means whereby throughout the metal a state with unpaired electrons having parallel spins has a lower energy than otherwise.

We introduce a quantity $\Delta E$, which is the energy required to reverse the direction of the spin of an electron without changing its wavenumber, at the absolute zero temperature. This is the same as the displacement in energy of the sub-band with positive spin relative to that with negative spin, when the magnetization is saturated. The state with spins parallel will always have the lower energy in order to satisfy Hund's rules, tending towards ferromagnetism. But this needs to overcome the small increase in the Fermi energy resulting from the setting up of a magnetic moment. The condition for ferromagnetism is

$$(2/n)\,\Delta E \; v(E_m)\,v > 1 \tag{5.4}$$

where $v(E_m)$ is the density of the states at the Fermi level, $v$ is of the atomic volume and $n$ is the excess number of spins per atom pointing in the direction of magnetization. This is really the condition that the total energy is lowered by a small polarization at the Fermi surface. An estimate of the value for the left-hand side of Equ. 5.4 based on experimental quantities gives 1·23 for nickel and 1·11 for iron, both of which thus satisfy this condition for ferromagnetism. The condition suggests that ferromagnetism should occur most readily when the density of states at the Fermi level is large, and when $\Delta E$ is relatively large. Under the conditions assumed here it would be expected that $\Delta E$ would be given by the product of:

(a) the energy difference, known experimentally from spectroscopic measurements, between the states of the free atom for which two spins of electrons in an incomplete d-shell are parallel or antiparallel; and

(b) the probability that an electron with a given direction of spin finds itself on the same atom as another electron with a spin which may be parallel or antiparallel.

Rough calculations of values for $\Delta E$ made along these lines for iron and for nickel show quite reasonable agreement with the best experimental estimates.

Once the existence of $\Delta E$ has been justified, the general basis of collective electron ferromagnetism becomes more sound. Comparing the nomenclature here with that of Chapter 3, $\Delta E$ is the same as $2\,k\theta'$. However, it is true to say that the question of exchange in electron bands which are relatively narrow, like those of 3d-metals, has not yet been solved satisfactorily. Other views concern what happens if the correlation energy is large and two magnetic carriers are inhibited from coming together on the same atom. Intra-atomic effects are then insignificant. It has not yet been possible to distinguish experimentally between the validity of the different points of view.

### 5.1.3    Superexchange

The magnetic coupling in many magnetic oxides and other similar materials cannot be explained by the mechanism of direct exchange because the ions on which the magnetic moment is known to be located are too far apart. Also, when the crystal structures of such materials are examined it is often found that a non-magnetic anion such as oxygen is situated in the line joining magnetic cations. If the materials are insulators, band mechanisms requiring fairly free transfer of electrons throughout a specimen are not likely to operate. Kramers (1934) and Anderson (1950) proposed a mechanism called superexchange. Spins of magnetic cations are coupled indirectly through intervening anions.

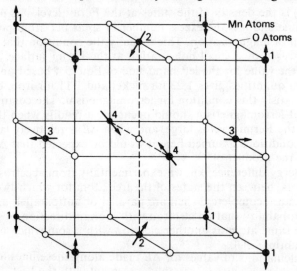

**Figure 5.2**    Magnetic structure of antiferromagnetic MnO. One magnetic unit cell is shown. Members of the four manganese sublattices are numbered. Nearest members of the same sublattice are strongly correlated, through intervening oxygen atoms. (After Anderson, 1950, *Phys. Rev.*, **79**, 350.)

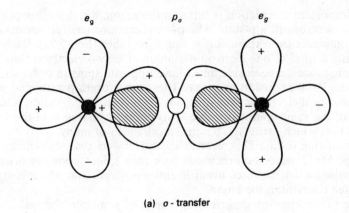

(a)  σ - transfer

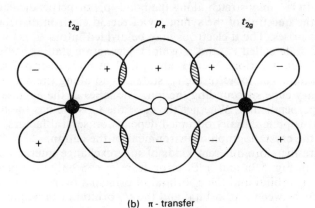

(b)  π - transfer

**Figure 5.3**  Superexchange. Kinds of electronic charge distribution round interacting cations and anions: (a) σ-transfer; and (b) π-transfer.

Superexchange is thought to operate in the antiferromagnetic compound MnO (Fig. 5.2). Its crystal structure is that of sodium chloride. $Mn^{2+}$ ions form a face-centred cubic structure which is interpenetrated by an identical face-centred cubic structure of $O^{2-}$ ions. $Mn^{2+}$ ions which are next-nearest neighbours have spins which are always antiparallel to each other. Lines joining these second neighbours always contain an anion $O^{2-}$ at the mid-point. First neighbour $Mn^{2+}$ ions are not strongly correlated, and no anion lies directly between them.

The important interaction is through the anion, which in this case has its outer electrons in a p-state. The p-wavefunctions (charge density) extend outwards from the anion in opposing lobes (Fig. 5.3a). Each lobe represents a total of one electron per anion. The two electrons thus represented, one on each side, must have opposite spins in order to satisfy the Pauli exclusion principle. These lobes overlap with, and mix with, lobes of d-electrons extending out from each $Mn^{2+}$ cation. Only mixing of the same spin is possible. This covalent mixing is of the same kind as that which forms the binding mechanism of many semiconducting solids. This mechanism thus lowers the total energy when the $Mn^{2+}$ cations on each side have their spins oppositely oriented, and provides a driving force towards antiferromagnetism which is strong in the line containing the anion.

While the mechanism described is correct in principle, the real situation is more complicated. The lobes representing the two 2p-electrons of $O^{2-}$ may stretch along the bond ($p_\sigma$) or perpendicular to it ($p_\pi$). And the question of the symmetry of the 3d-electron distribution of the cations arises. The d-electrons may be divided into a threefold degenerate state called $t_{2g}$ and a twofold degenerate state called $e_g$. This is the Mulliken notation. There is an equivalent but rather different Bethe notation. The lobes of the $t_{2g}$ state extend along the diagonals of an imaginary cube surrounding the ion. The lobes of the $e_g$ state are mutually perpendicular. Whether the $e_g$ or the $t_{2g}$ state has the lower energy and is preferentially occupied depends on several factors, including the crystallographic environment of the cation.

There are therefore different kinds of superexchange interaction, illustrated in Fig. 5.3a and b. Electron transfer can only take place between a $p_\sigma$ orbital and the $e_g$ orbital of principal overlap (called $\sigma$-transfer), or between a $p_\pi$ orbital and the $t_{2g}$ orbital of principal overlap (called $\pi$-transfer). For a given interatomic separation the orbital overlap involved in $\sigma$-transfer is greater than it is in $\pi$-transfer, as Fig. 5.3 would seem to indicate. A $\sigma$-transfer process is therefore the stronger. In a given situation, depending on the circumstances either or both $\sigma$- or $\pi$-transfer may operate, with corresponding variations in the strength of the overall superexchange interaction. By and large, theory based along the lines indicated offers quite a good explanation of magnetic interactions in non-metallic magnetically ordered materials.

Processes may sometimes be modified by the operation of cation–anion–cation interactions at $90°$ or other angles different from $180°$. In special cases there may be direct overlap of the diagonal $t_{2g}$ orbitals of first-neighbour cations, or between $t_{2g}$ of one atom and $e_g$ of the other. This is direct exchange. It would generally be a relatively weak and very much separation-dependent contribution to the total effect and might be positive (ferromagnetic) or negative (antiferromagnetic) in sign.

### 5.1.4  Indirect exchange by polarization of the conduction electrons

An important mechanism of magnetic coupling between localized magnetic moments in metals depends on the ability of conduction electrons to interact magnetically with the local moments and to propagate between different magnetic sites. How the conduction electrons can polarize and propagate was first shown by Ruderman and Kittel (1954). They dealt with nuclear magnetic moments immersed in a distribution of conduction electrons. Kasuya and then Yosida developed and extended the theory to s–f and s–d interactions. The mechanism has become known as the RKKY theory. The spin polarization of the conduction electrons is not localized in the vicinity of the local moment but is oscillatory and long-ranged. The mechanism can be simply visualized as follows.

Consider a single localized magnetic moment surrounded by a gas of conduction electrons. The local moment is on a lattice site in the metal. The effect of the local moment is to make the site on which it is placed a region favourable for a conduction electron of parallel magnetic moment but unfavourable for an electron of antiparallel moment. In order to take advantage of the magnetic interaction, a parallel electron will distort its wavefunction so as to be larger in the vicinity of the local moment. This is brought about by mixing in other electron states of the same spin orientation. The result is as though only states above the Fermi level are added. The wavefunctions of the added states are such that they are all in phase with each other at the position of the local moment, so that they may interfere constructively at that point. Since they must correspond to a range of wavevectors and therefore a range of wavelengths, they must get out of step as the distance from the local moment increases, and begin to interfere destructively (Fig. 5.4a). The original uniform distribution of electrons with parallel spin is changed to have an oscillatory behaviour which dies out as the distance from the local moment increases.

Likewise, conduction electrons with antiparallel spin distort their wavefunctions so as to be smaller in the vicinity of the local moment. In just the same way this produces a corresponding oscillatory absence of antiparallel spin. The overall effect is to give an oscillatory distribution of spin density in the region of the local moment (Fig. 5.4b). Since the attraction of electrons with parallel spin is exactly matched by the repulsion of those with antiparallel spin at all points, and all have the same charge, the distribution of charge density remains uniform throughout. The periodicity of the spin density oscillation is set by the

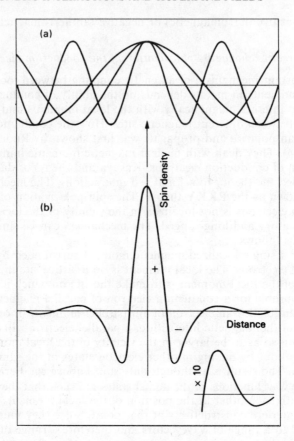

**Figure 5.4**   RKKY interaction. (a) Wavefunctions of interacting conduction electrons near a magnetic impurity; and (b) the resultant distribution of conduction electron spin density.

wavelengths of the conduction electrons at the Fermi level. That is, it is dominated by the Fermi momentum. The exact form of the spin density distribution and its variation with distance must depend on how the electron wavelength varies with energy at the Fermi level, which is given by the $(E,k)$ relationship. The RKKY theory was worked out for free electrons having a spherical Fermi surface and as such represents a simplification. More complicated situations have not yet been investigated widely.

When a second atom bearing a local magnetic moment is situated at an arbitrary distance from the first it interacts ferromagnetically or antiferromagnetically depending on whether it is in a positive or a negative part of the polarization wave from the first atom. According to the RKKY theory the strength of the magnetic coupling between atoms a relatively large distance $R$ apart varies according to

$$(1/R^3)\cos(2\,k_F R) \tag{5.5}$$

where $k_F$ represents the Fermi momentum.

The most important properties of this mechanism of magnetic coupling are the following. First, the magnetic interaction has a long-range character, certainly of much longer range than any direct exchange involving charge overlap between adjacent atoms. Second, quite large variations in the strength of the interaction and even reversal of its sign are possible with small changes in the relationship between the interatomic distance and the periodicity of the spin density.

### 5.1.5   Experimental confirmation of the RKKY model

The RKKY model appears to apply well to some dilute magnetic alloys, such as dilute solutions of manganese in copper. The manganese atoms are probably in either $3d^4$- or $3d^5$-states, carrying corresponding local magnetic moments of $4\mu_B$ or $5\mu_B$. At a concentration of about 0·01 at. % of Mn each manganese atom is surrounded on average by $(0\cdot01\,\%)^{-1} = 10^4$ copper atoms, or in a face-centred cubic structure (4 atoms per unit cell) by 2500 unit cells. These would be contained in a sphere of radius about thirteen times the lattice parameter. Yet it is known that such an alloy is antiferromagnetic at low temperatures. This was the alloy system to which Yosida first applied the theory. The detailed experimental observations on the nuclear magnetic resonance and the electron spin resonance properties were explained well. Also, Kondo showed that interactions of the kind described give a natural description of the minima in graphs of electrical resistance against temperature for many dilute alloys.

In the rare-earth metals there is little possibility of direct overlap interactions between the 4f-electrons of adjacent atoms. These electrons are too well screened and the radius of their shells is relatively small. Indirect exchange through the conduction electrons allows them to become magnetically ordered. The spiral and other non-collinear magnetic structures that are fairly common in the rare earths and their alloys are a result of differing strengths and signs of interaction at different interatomic neighbour distances.

### 5.1.6 *Magnetic interactions which differ between different atomic neighbours*

It is clearly to be expected that when the magnetic interaction is of long range and its strength depends on the interatomic distance, there will be situations in which the nearest-neighbour interaction does not dominate the others completely. Sometimes significant interactions might be expected to have opposite signs. Under certain conditions helical magnetic structures can result.

A crystal structure having uniaxial symmetry, such as a hexagonal or a tetragonal structure, is the simplest case to consider. The magnetic atoms are arranged in parallel layers perpendicular to the $c$-axis. A simplifying assumption is that effects of magnetocrystalline anisotropy act to confine the atomic moments to lie within the planes of the layers. The exchange coupling constants $J_n$ are defined as follows:

$J_0$ refers to pairs of atoms in the same layer (assumed positive here),

$J_1$ refers to pairs of atoms each situated in adjacent layers,

$J_2$ refers to pairs of atoms each situated in second nearest layers, etc.

These exchange constants can be regarded in a molecular field model as being equivalent to molecular field coefficients $\gamma_0$, $\gamma_1$, $\gamma_2$, etc. The angle between the spin directions of adjacent layers is $\alpha$, and it is not assumed that this is necessarily $0°$ or $180°$. The total molecular field acting on the atoms of the central layer is now

$$(B_0)_{\text{mol}} = \gamma_0\,\sigma_0 + 2\gamma_1\,\sigma_1 \cos\alpha + 2\gamma_2\,\sigma_2 \cos 2\alpha + \ldots \tag{5.6}$$

where $\sigma_n$ is the magnetization of the $n$th layer. There are equivalent neighbouring layers both above and below the central layer. If all the layers are equivalent their magnetizations are the same and $\sigma_0 = \sigma_1 = \sigma_2 = \ldots$ Then

$$(B_0)_{\text{mol}} = \sigma(\gamma_0 + 2\gamma_1 \cos\alpha + 2\gamma_2 \cos 2\alpha + \ldots) = \sigma\,\gamma(\alpha) \tag{5.7}$$

Since the exchange energy is the self-energy of the magnetic moment in the molecular field

$$E_{\text{ex}} = -\int_0^\sigma B_0\,\mathrm{d}\sigma = -\tfrac{1}{2}\gamma(\alpha)\,\sigma^2 \tag{5.8}$$

This varies with temperature through the variation of the magnetization with temperature. At a given temperature, the equilibrium interlayer turn angle $\alpha_0$ is that value for which the exchange energy is a minimum. This is where $\gamma(\alpha) = (\gamma_0 + 2\gamma_1 \cos\alpha + 2\gamma_2 \cos 2\alpha + \ldots)$ is a maximum.

If $\gamma_1, \gamma_2, \ldots$ are all positive the maximum value of $\gamma(\alpha)$ is where $\alpha_0 = 0$.

This is a ferromagnetic state, with all the layers magnetized in the same direction. If $\gamma_1$ is negative and $\gamma_2$, $\gamma_3$, ... are all zero, the maximum value of $\gamma(\alpha)$ is where $\cos\alpha = -1$, or $\alpha_0 = 180°$. This is simple antiferromagnetism, with the spins of alternate layers pointing in opposite directions. When $\gamma_3$, $\gamma_4$, ... are insignificant, with $\gamma_1$ and $\gamma_2$ of opposite sign and $\gamma_2$ having a magnitude at least $\gamma_1/4$ the magnetic structure is helical. The interlayer turn angle $\alpha_0$ is given by

$$\cos\alpha_0 = -\gamma_1/4\gamma_2 \tag{5.9}$$

Different external constraints or initial conditions give rise to different magnetic structures, and the complication of the treatment increases as higher orders of neighbour interaction become significant. Not all the structures are non-collinear. Some of the more complicated antiferromagnetic structures are fairly well understood in terms of particular relationships between higher-neighbour interactions.

In metals the principal mechanism by which significant interactions of either sign between a central atom and its neighbours at different distances can occur is the RKKY mechanism.

## 5.2   Hyperfine interactions in magnetic materials

Hyperfine interactions are interactions between atomic nuclei and the electrons which surround them. Their name arises from the way in which the interactions were first observed, by their effect on spectra in the visible region of the spectrum. The interactions may be studied by making observations on nuclear properties. It is useful to investigate the interactions in solid materials because of the information that they can give about the properties of extranuclear electrons and about the solid-state interatomic interactions which involve these electrons.

Several experimental techniques are involved. These often give overlapping or complementary information, on some or all of the following.

(1) The magnetic interaction between the nucleus and the electrons. This depends linearly on the nuclear spin $I$. It is expressed as the hyperfine magnetic field $B_H$. It should be noted that this is quite different from the Weiss molecular field, or any other molecular field which expresses the exchange interaction in magnetically ordered systems.

(2) The electrostatic interaction between the nucleus and the electrons. This varies in a quadratic way with the nuclear spin. It is the nuclear quadrupole interaction, between the nuclear quadrupole moment (if it is not zero) and the gradient of the electric field in which it is situated.

(3) Electron density effects at the nucleus. This is observed as the isomer shift in experiments using the Mössbauer effect.

Experiments which give information on hyperfine interactions include the following:
the Mössbauer effect
nuclear magnetic resonance
nuclear specific heats.

### 5.2.1  The Mössbauer effect

The Mössbauer effect arises from a special property of the emission and absorption of $\gamma$-rays by nuclei of atoms that are bound in a crystal lattice. It leads essentially to a form of spectroscopy having a much higher intrinsic resolving power than that of any other form of spectroscopy.

When a free atom at rest emits a $\gamma$-ray photon it recoils with kinetic energy

$$R = \tfrac{1}{2}E_0{}^2/(M c^2)$$

where $E_0$ is the energy of the nuclear transition, $M$ is the mass of the atom and $c$ is the velocity of light. The emitted $\gamma$-ray photon thus has the energy $E_\gamma = E_0 - R$. Similarly for the absorption process in another atom, for resonance absorption to occur the incident photon must have energy $E'_\gamma = E_0 + R$. In general, because of the Doppler effect due to thermal motion, broad emission and absorption spectra occur centred on $E_\gamma$ and $E'_\gamma$, as shown in Fig. 5.5. The overlap of the two spectra is small and little resonance absorption is expected. Increasing the temperature was at first expected to widen each peak in Fig. 5.5 by increasing the Doppler broadening, and to increase the resonance absorption.

Mössbauer found that in some cases reducing the temperature produced a marked increase in the resonance absorption. When the source was given a small additional Doppler velocity (of the order of 1 cm s$^{-1}$) with respect to the absorber, sharp peaks could be traced out. These were centred on the resonance energy $E_0$ and had the natural linewidth of the nuclear transition. $\Delta v/v$ was of the order of $10^{-12}$ ($v$ is the frequency of the $\gamma$-ray).

The reason for the effect is that recoil-less emission and absorption of $\gamma$-rays can occur. In a solid, each atom is confined by its neighbours and at low temperatures there is a finite probability that the recoil momentum will be taken up by the crystal as a whole, without emission or absorption of phonons (quantized lattice vibrations). Since the mass of the crystal is effectively infinite the recoil energy will be very small. Once recoil-less emission and absorption can occur, large resonance absorption is possible. Since the lines are so sharp they can be traced out by applying small energy displacements between source and absorber

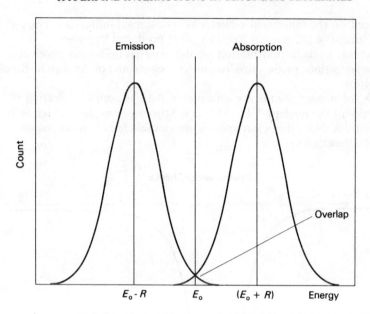

**Figure 5.5**  $\gamma$-ray emission and absorption spectra for free atoms, showing the displacements due to recoil and the small amount of overlap.

by way of a small change in the relative velocity between them, using the Doppler effect. A typical absorption curve for a single nuclear transition is shown in Fig. 5.6.

Because of its extreme resolution the Mössbauer effect makes possible the analysis of the hyperfine structure of nuclear transitions, and in particular the observation of the nuclear Zeeman effect.

The magnetic moment of the nucleus can interact with an externally applied magnetic field or with unpaired electrons on its own atom and its neighbours. The magnetic interaction with electrons is of two types. For s-electrons it is a contact interaction proportional to the electron density at the nucleus of the unpaired electrons, and for other electrons it is a dipole–dipole interaction.

It is the innermost atomic electrons which contribute most to the contact interaction. A single 1s-electron can produce an effective magnetic field at the nucleus of about 300 000 T ($3 \times 10^9$ Oe). However, the 1s, 2s, 3s... electrons exist usually in balanced pairs predominantly, with equal numbers of opposite spins which tend to cancel out the interaction field. The interaction observed is usually due to the effect of unpaired outer s-electrons in the atoms, or is due to core polarization produced on the innermost s-electrons by external influences. Thus measurement of the nuclear Zeeman effect produced by these interactions leads to information on the external influences producing core polarization; or on unpaired outer s-electrons; or on dipole–dipole interactions.

How the measurements are interpreted may be seen by referring to the properties of the nucleus $^{57}$Fe. This is a Mössbauer nucleus which is in common use. Not all nuclear species are suitable for observations on the Mössbauer effect.

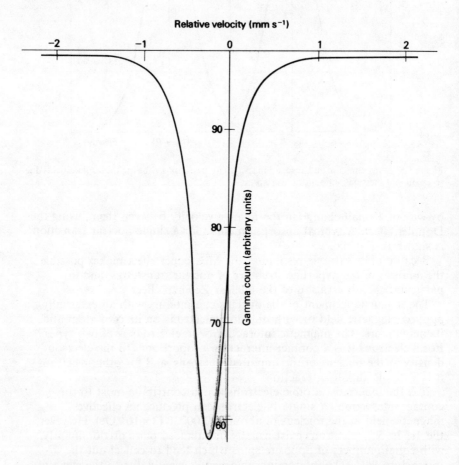

**Figure 5.6** Paramagnetic Mössbauer spectrum with an absorber of stainless steel. The displacement of the central absorption from zero is the isomer shift. (By courtesy of J. Williams.)

Starting with the nucleus $^{57}Co$, this decays radioactively with a half-life of 270 days to an excited state of $^{57}Fe$ (Fig. 5.7), this state having a nuclear spin quantum number $I = \frac{5}{2}$. This falls to its ground state ($I = \frac{1}{2}$) either directly (9%) or via the intermediate state (91%) which has $I = \frac{3}{2}$. The $I = \frac{3}{2}$ state has an energy of 14·4 keV above the ground state and a lifetime $\tau = 1\cdot4 \times 10^{-7}$ s.

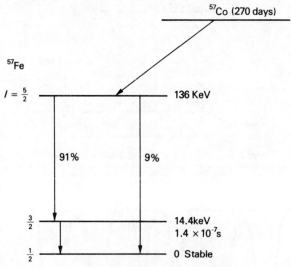

**Figure 5.7**   Decay system of $^{57}Fe$.

It is the transition between $I = \frac{3}{2}$ and $I = \frac{1}{2}$ which is used here. When there is no magnetic or electric field present the transition is of a single energy since both levels are degenerate. This produces the single Mössbauer line of Fig. 5.6. In a magnetic field both levels split by an amount which is proportional to the field (Fig. 5.8). The selection rule for transitions is that $\Delta m_I = \pm 1$ or 0, leading in this case to six different transition energies and six lines in the Zeeman spectrum (Fig. 5.9). From the positions of the lines the splitting of the levels may be evaluated, and hence the strength of the effective magnetic field which acts.

There are additional effects which are not of primary concern here, due to any electric field gradient which may be present and to the average density of electrons at the nucleus. When the nuclear charge is not spherically symmetrical the presence of an electric field gradient can split the energy levels. This is nuclear quadrupole splitting. Also, the ground state and the excited state of the nucleus have slightly different charge radii, causing a small change in the overlap energy with an

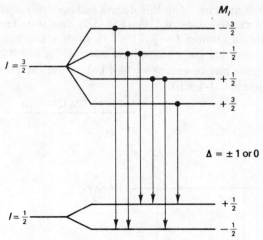

**Figure 5.8**    Energy level splitting scheme for $^{57}$Fe.

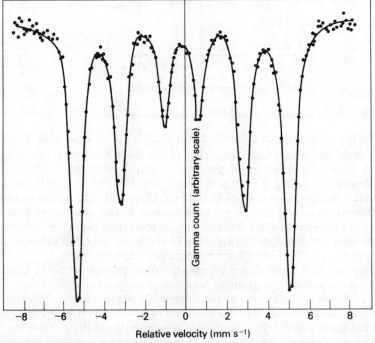

**Figure 5.9**    Six-line Mössbauer absorption spectrum for $^{57}$Fe contained in a ferromagnet. (By courtesy of J. Williams.)

overlying electronic charge. This has the effect of moving the whole Mössbauer pattern sideways to a different energy. It is called the isomer shift.

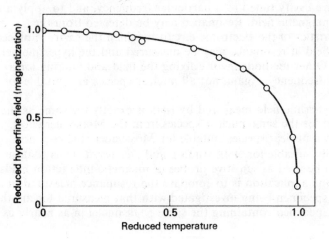

**Figure 5.10** Hyperfine field in ferromagnetic iron normalized to its value at $T = 0$ plotted against the reduced temperature. The experimental points are from Mössbauer measurements. (From Preston *et al.*, 1962, *Phys. Rev.*, **128**, 2207.) The full line is for the spontaneous magnetization similarly normalized.

Fig. 5.10 illustrates the sensitivity of the Mössbauer hyperfine field in iron to the magnetization of the environment. The hyperfine field is closely related to the average spontaneous magnetization of the whole specimen. A typical hyperfine field is 30 T $= 3 \times 10^5$ Oe.

### 5.2.2 *Nuclear magnetic resonance*

When a nucleus having a nuclear magnetic moment $\mu_N$ and total angular momentum $I h/2\pi$ is placed in a magnetic field $B_0$ it has magnetic energy

$$E_m = -\mu_N B_0$$

An equal splitting of the $(2I + 1)$ sub-levels is produced. The energy separation between adjacent sub-levels is

$$\Delta E = B_0 g_I h/2\pi$$

where $g_I$ is the nuclear $g$-factor. There can be resonance absorption of electromagnetic radiation of frequency $v$ or angular frequency $\omega$, where $v = \Delta E/h$ or $\omega = (2\pi/h)\Delta E$. The field $B_0$ may be made up of contributions from an externally applied field and a hyperfine field $B_H$.

The resonant absorptions may be observed in a number of ways. One method is to place a sample of the material being investigated in a microwave cavity tuned to a particular frequency, and to apply a slowly varying magnetic field. Resonance may be detected from the characteristics of the electronic circuit in which the cavity is placed. The applied field at resonance may be measured and the hyperfine field derived. Other methods involve fixing the field and looking for a resonant frequency. Again, not all nuclear species are suitable for NMR studies.

The hyperfine field measured by NMR is exactly the same as that measured for the same nuclear species from the Mössbauer effect. However, a nuclear species suitable for Mössbauer studies is not necessarily suitable for NMR studies, and *vice versa*. Thus NMR nuclei may also be used as sensitive probes of magnetic interaction fields in solids. One application is to compare the resonance measured in a metallic specimen being investigated with that measured for another non-metallic specimen containing the same NMR nuclei in as nearly as

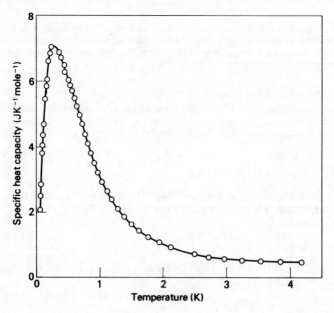

**Figure 5.11**   The specific heat capacity of holmium at low temperatures, showing the nuclear contribution. (Data from Lounasmaa, 1962, *Phys. Rev.*, **128**, 1136 and van Kempen, Miedema and Huiskamp, 1964, *Physica*, **30**, 229.)

possible the same environment except for the absence of the metallic state. The shift in resonance frequency is called the Knight shift. It is due to the overlap with the nucleus of s-conduction electrons polarized paramagnetically by the applied magnetic field. It thus gives a measure of properties of s-electrons near the Fermi level in the metal.

### 5.2.3   Nuclear contributions to the specific heat capacity

As we have seen already, when a nucleus with angular momentum quantum number $I$ is acted upon by a magnetic field, $(2I + 1)$ sub-levels, all having different energies are produced. At high temperatures these are all filled statistically in accordance with the thermal energy available. When the temperature is reduced to a low level there is a redistribution among the energy levels and the energy associated with the redistribution shows up as a contribution $c_N$ of Schottky type (Fig. 5.11) to the total specific heat capacity. This gives information on the energy spacing of the sub-levels and hence on the magnitude of the hyperfine field giving rise to the splitting of levels. The nuclear heat capacity $c_N$ has its maximum at that temperature $T_m$ at which

$$kT_m \simeq \mu_N B_H / I$$

Because of the smallness of nuclear magnetic moments this is usually at temperatures of the order of $10^{-1}$ or $10^{-2}$ K.

Among other experiments not discussed here which give information on hyperfine interactions are electron spin resonance and the scattering of polarized neutrons.

# 6
# Domain Magnetism

## 6.1 Basic principles of domain magnetism

It is possible to obtain an unmagnetized piece of ferromagnetic material such as iron by suitable treatment with an alternating field of decreasing amplitude. Starting with the demagnetized state and applying an increasing unidirectional field the magnetization increases, slowly and reversibly at first, but thereafter quickly and irreversibly and finally slowly until eventually the saturated state is reached. Two very significant features that are found are first that cases exist where magnetic saturation may be reached in weak fields of the order of $10^{-6}$ T ($10^{-2}$ Oe), and the second that the magnetization of the same specimen may be zero in zero field.

It is known from the study of paramagnetism that applying such small fields has an entirely negligible effect on the magnetization of a system of free and independent elementary magnetic moments. The properties observed are explained by the presence of separate magnetized regions in the ferromagnetic sample called domains. Each domain is intrinsically fully magnetized under the influence of exchange interactions described by a molecular field. Changes in overall magnetization in relatively low fields are almost all due to re-arrangements of domains and the boundaries between them. The demagnetized state is one where the overall magnetization of the collection of separate domains all differently oriented cancels out.

The reason for the formation of the domain structure is that the potential energy associated with the magnetized sample is thereby minimized. This is in spite of the cost in energy of forming the domain boundaries.

Studies of domain properties in ferromagnets tend to be on the properties of either soft or of hard magnetic materials. The technological aim of such work is to improve soft materials by making it possible for domain boundaries to sweep through the solid with the minimum constraint. In hard materials the usual aim is to lock the magnetized state into position as permanently as possible. Technical applications of domain properties are described more fully in Chapter 8. The range of coercivities (see § 1.1.1) found experimentally is from about $2 \times 10^{-7}$ T $(2 \times 10^{-3}$ Oe) in supermalloy transformers to about 1 T $(10^4$ Oe) in $SmCo_5$ high-stability magnets.

Crystal orientation is important when domain properties are considered. Due to magnetocrystalline anisotropy differing energies are involved in magnetizing a specimen in different crystallographic directions. Much of the earlier part of the discussion here refers to the properties of single crystals having selected orientations. In polycrystalline specimens there is usually a randomly oriented array of small crystallites. Sometimes a magnetic material is heterogeneous, consisting of islands of a strongly magnetized phase embedded in a matrix of a weakly magnetized or non-ferromagnetic phase.

### 6.1.1  Magnetocrystalline anisotropy

The potential energy of a single crystal sample of a ferromagnet depends on the direction with respect to the crystal axes in which it is magnetized. The energy is lowest in an easy direction and a higher field must be applied to make the magnetization lie in a harder direction. This is illustrated for iron, cobalt and nickel in Fig. 1.4.

Hexagonal cobalt is uniaxial, having only a single easy direction along the hexagonal axis. The magnetocrystalline energy of a uniaxial ferromagnet is written empirically as a series

$$E_k = K_1 \sin^2\theta + K_2 \sin^4\theta + \ldots = \sum_n K_n \sin^{2n}\theta \qquad (6.1)$$

where $K_1, K_2, \ldots$ are empirical constants which vary with temperature and which differ for different materials. $\theta$ is the angle between the magnetization vector and the direction of the crystallographic axis. Odd powers of $\sin\theta$ do not appear because the series must be symmetrical with respect to either direction along the easy axis.

In iron any of the three cube edge directions are directions of easy magnetization. The energy of a cubic crystal may be written

$$E_k = K_0 + K_1(\alpha_1^2\alpha_2^2 + \alpha_1^2\alpha_3^2 + \alpha_2^2\alpha_3^2) + K_2(\alpha_1^2\alpha_2^2\alpha_3^2) + \ldots \qquad (6.2)$$

where $\alpha_1, \alpha_2, \alpha_3$ are the direction cosines of the magnetization direction with respect to the cubic axes of the crystal.

In each case the series is short, the magnitude of the anisotropy constant $K_n$ decreasing rapidly with increasing $n$ and becoming lost in experimental error.

In cubic crystals the easy directions are along the cube edges if $K_1$ is positive and $K_2$ is not more negative than $-\frac{9}{4}K_1$. When $K_1$ is negative, as for nickel, the easy directions are along the cube diagonals.

The order of magnitude of the magnetocrystalline energies involved is given by the values of $K_1$ for different materials (at room temperature) shown in Table 6.1.

**Table 6.1**  First anisotropy constants $K_1$.

| Material | $K_1 (\mathrm{J\,m^{-3}})$ | $K_1 (\mathrm{erg\,cm^{-3}})$ |
|---|---|---|
| Fe | $4{\cdot}7 \times 10^4$ | $4{\cdot}7 \times 10^5$ |
| Co | $4{\cdot}1 \times 10^5$ | $4{\cdot}1 \times 10^6$ |
| Ni | $5{\cdot}1 \times 10^3$ | $5{\cdot}1 \times 10^4$ |
| SmCo$_5$ | $1{\cdot}1 \times 10^7$ | $1{\cdot}1 \times 10^8$ |

The effect of this energy on the domain structure is that it imposes a constraint on the direction that the magnetization takes up in a given crystal when no external field is applied. And it also makes an important contribution to the intrinsic energy of domain boundary walls and controls their thickness.

In materials in which the magnetism comes from atoms and ions of the first transition series the magnetic moments are due to spin moments, mainly of 3d-electrons, and these are not coupled directly with the crystal lattice. Here the magnetic anisotropy energy arises from the indirect coupling of the spins with the lattice *via* the spin–orbit coupling and the orbit–lattice coupling. The extent to which a magnetic ion feels the symmetry of the lattice depends strongly and in a fairly complicated way on its electronic structure and a wide variety of cases occurs.

Where the source of the magnetism is rare-earth atoms and ions the magnetic moments consist of both orbital and spin moments. There is here a direct coupling between orbital moment and lattice and the resultant magnetic anisotropy is usually much stronger than for the indirectly coupled transition series materials.

### 6.1.2  *Magnetostatic energy*

When a ferromagnetic body is isolated and placed in a saturating field $B_0$ the effect at its end surfaces is as though free magnetic poles ('magnetic charge') are present. The effect is produced by the discontinuity at the surfaces of the normal component of magnetization; or otherwise when the magnetization is internally non-uniform. The field $(B_0)_i$ acting inside the body may be written

$$(B_0)_i = B_0 - (B_0)_D \tag{6.3}$$

where $(B_0)_D$ is a demagnetizing field. It is that which would be produced by the apparent surface pole distribution acting in isolation.

The demagnetizing field applies to all magnetized materials, even weak paramagnets, although sometimes its effect is small. Its magnitude depends on the shape of the specimen and on the magnetization $M$. The demagnetizing factor $D$ is defined by

$$(B_0)_D = DM \tag{6.4}†$$

$D$ has been tabulated for ellipsoids of revolution, for which the calculation is exact (Fig. 6.1). $D$ may be calculated approximately for other figures. Rectangular rods of square cross section have values of $D$ close to those for ellipsoids having the same ratio of length ($l$) to breadth ($b$). For $l/b > 1$, $D$ is roughly proportional to $(l/b)^{-1}$. When the specimen is longer and thinner, the demagnetizing field is smaller.

The magnetostatic energy per unit volume of the body when it is in an external field $B_0$ is the sum of two terms depending respectively on the internal and the external fields:

$$E_m = -\tfrac{1}{2}(B_0)_i.M - B_0.M \tag{6.5}$$

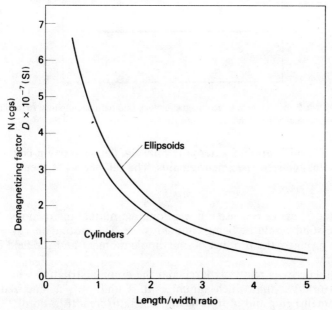

**Figure 6.1** Demagnetizing factors for ellipsoids and cylinders.

†In CGS $(H)_D = N I$
where $N = 4\pi D/\mu_0$

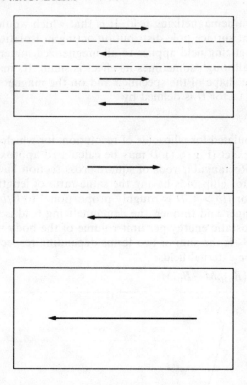

**Figure 6.2**  Division of rectangular ferromagnetic block into parallel domains. Arrows indicate magnitude of demagnetizing field.

When no field is applied externally only the demagnetizing field of the uniformly magnetized specimen remains. The self-energy is then

$$E_s = +\tfrac{1}{2} DM^2 \qquad (6.6)$$

The factor $\tfrac{1}{2}$ arises because if it were omitted mutual interactions within the solid would be being counted twice. The mutual energy of two dipoles is given by the product of one dipole moment and the field due to the other.

This self-energy is relatively large and the domain structure which occurs naturally is that which minimizes it. A uniformly magnetized (single domain) ellipsoid of iron having a length/breadth ratio of 3·0 would have a self-energy of about $1 \cdot 7 \times 10^5$ J m$^{-3}$ ($1 \cdot 7 \times 10^6$ erg cm$^{-3}$).

In a rectangular body magnetized along its length (Fig. 6.2), changing from a single domain to two equal oppositely magnetized domains reduces the self-energy to about one half. This is because the ratio of length to breadth of each domain is doubled, the demagnetizing field therefore approximately halved. This reduction in energy through domains narrowing cannot continue indefinitely, because it must be set against the increase in energy due to the necessary creation of new domain boundaries.

### 6.1.3    Domain boundary walls (Bloch walls)

A domain boundary wall (Fig. 6.3) consists of the transition layer which separates adjacent domains magnetized in different directions. The total angular displacement across a wall is commonly 180° or 90°. In general, the whole change in spin direction does not occur in one discontinuous jump at a single atomic plane but it takes place gradually over many planes. What determines the thickness (width) of a wall is a compromise between the opposing influences of exchange energy and magnetocrystalline anisotropy energy.

Following Equ. 5.3 the increase in exchange energy between two spins displaced through a small angle $\phi$ from their equilibrium parallel alignment is

$$\Delta e_{ex} = J S^2 \phi^2 \tag{6.7}$$

where $J$ is the exchange integral and $S$ is the spin quantum number. If

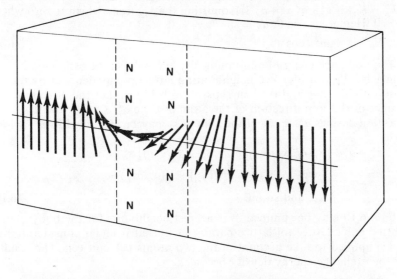

**Figure 6.3**   Domain boundary wall. (After Kittel, 1949, *Rev. Mod. Phys.*, **21**, 561.)

E

the total angular displacement across the wall is $\phi_0$, made in $N$ steps over a line of $N+1$ atoms, the total energy of the line is

$$\Delta E_{ex} = J S^2 \phi_0^2/N \tag{6.8}$$

Thus the exchange energy of a line of atoms perpendicular to the wall is inversely proportional to the number of steps in the line. A wall 101 atoms thick has exchange energy only $1/100$ of the energy of a wall in which all the angular change is between two neighbours.

The thickness and the energy of a domain wall may be estimated for particular cases. One important case, which we consider here, is that of a wall parallel to a (001) plane in iron, which separates domains magnetized in opposite directions. The direction of the magnetization of the adjacent domains are taken as [100] ($x$ direction) and [$\bar{1}$00] ($-x$ direction). The $z$ direction is normal to the domain wall.

The rotation of the spin direction on passing through the wall is such that the spin always lies in the plane of the wall. This is the result for the case considered here of the general requirement that the normal component of the magnetization shall remain constant through the wall. This is determined by the condition for minimum magnetostatic energy, with no free poles being formed.

Let $\theta$ be the angle between the spin direction and the $x$-axis. Thus $\theta$ varies from 0 to $\pi = 180°$. The magnetocrystalline anisotropy energy density in the $(x,y)$ plane is then (from Equ. 6.2)

$E_k = K_1(\alpha_1^2 \alpha_2^2 + \alpha_1^2 \alpha_3^2 + \alpha_2^2 \alpha_3^2)$, omitting the $K_2$ term, which is zero when $\alpha_3 = 0$. Here $\alpha_1 = \cos\theta$; $\alpha_2 = \sin\theta$; $\alpha_3 = 0$, so

$$E_k = K_1 \sin^2\theta \cos^2\theta \tag{6.9}$$

The exchange energy ('non-uniformity energy') can be estimated similarly. We consider two neighbouring lattice points denoted by the position vectors $r_i$ and $r_j$, their separation being $r_{ij}$. Let the direction cosines of the spin direction of the atom at $r_j$ be $\alpha_j^x$, $\alpha_j^y$, $\alpha_j^z$. Now the direction cosines $\alpha_i^x$, $\alpha_i^y$, $\alpha_i^z$ of the spin at $r_i$ may be expanded in a Taylor series

$$\alpha_i^x = \alpha_j^x + [x_{ij}(\partial/\partial x_{ij}) + y_{ij}(\partial/\partial y_{ij}) + z_{ij}(\partial/\partial z_{ij})]\,\alpha_j^x$$
$$+ \tfrac{1}{2}[x_{ij}^2(\partial^2/\partial x_{ij}) + y_{ij}(\partial^2/\partial y_{ij}) + z_{ij}(\partial^2/\partial z_{ij})]\,\alpha_j^x$$
$$+ \dots, \text{ and so on.} \tag{6.10}$$

Equ. 6.10 may be summed over nearest neighbours for the body-centred cubic lattice (of lattice parameter $a$) that is under consideration; and simplified to take account of the two atoms per unit cell. The result for the exchange energy density becomes

$$E_{ex} = (2J S^2/a)[(\nabla\alpha_1)^2 + (\nabla\alpha_2)^2 + (\nabla\alpha_3)^2] \tag{6.11}$$

In the present case, since $\alpha_1 = \cos\theta$; $\alpha_2 = \sin\theta$; $\alpha_3 = 0$, we have

$$E_{ex} = A\,(d\theta/dz)^2 \tag{6.12}$$

where $A = 2J\,S^2/a$.

Because the exchange theory is inexact various supposedly self-consistent experimental parameters lead to different values for $A$. The value derived from the low-temperature dependence of magnetization on temperature is related to spin-wave theory, which is itself closely allied to the behaviour of domain boundary walls. For iron this leads to a value of the exchange interaction parameter $J = 205\,k$, where $k$ is Boltzmann's constant. If we assume $S = 1$ (two spins per atom) and putting $a = 2\cdot86$ Å, we obtain

$$A = 2JS^2/a \simeq 2\times10^{-11}\ \text{Jm}^{-1}\,(= 2\times10^{-6}\ \text{erg cm}^{-1})$$

The total wall energy per unit area, $E_{wall}$, is the sum of the energies given by equations 6.9 and 6.12, integrated over the whole wall:

$$E_{wall} = \int_{-\infty}^{+\infty} [K_1\sin^2\theta\cos^2\theta + A\,(d\theta/dz)^2]\,dz \tag{6.13}$$

In equation 6.13 $\theta$ is to be determined as that function of $z$ which minimizes the total energy. The full derivation is not given here, but an important intermediate result is that for all values of $z$

$$K_1\sin^2\theta\cos^2\theta = A\,(d\theta/dz)^2 \tag{6.14}$$

This shows that at every point of the domain wall the local anisotropy energy density is equal to the local exchange energy density. In directions of high anisotropy energy neighbouring spins make larger angles with each other than in directions of low anisotropy energy.

The solution is of the form

$$\cos\theta = \tanh\left[z\,(K_1/A)^{\frac12}\right] \tag{6.15}$$

where $z$ is measured from the centre of the wall. This is illustrated in Fig. 6.4.

From Equ. 6.14

$$dz = (A/K_1)^{\frac12}\,\frac{d\theta}{\sin\theta\cos\theta} \tag{6.16}$$

Substituting for $dz$ and $d\theta/dz$ in Equ. 6.13 gives for the wall energy (per unit area)

$$E_{wall} = 2(K_1A)^{\frac12}\int_0^{\pi} |\sin\theta\cos\theta|\,d\theta = 2(K_1A)^{\frac12} \tag{6.17}$$

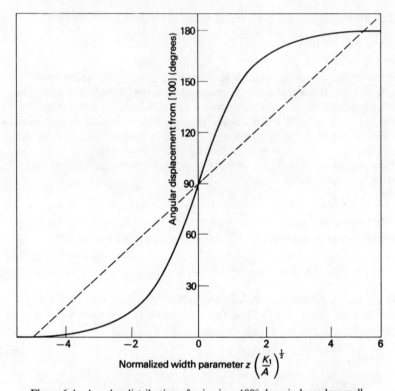

**Figure 6.4**  Angular distribution of spins in a 180° domain boundary wall.

Thus the wall energy for iron at room temperature is of the order of

$$2 \times (2 \times 10^{-11} \times 4 \cdot 7 \times 10^4)^{1/2} = 1 \cdot 94 \times 10^{-3} \, \text{Jm}^{-2} (= 1 \cdot 94 \, \text{erg cm}^{-2})$$

The order of magnitude of the 'thickness' of the domain boundary wall is

$$\delta \simeq \pi (A/K_1)^{\frac{1}{2}} \tag{6.18}$$

The factor $(A/K_1)^{\frac{1}{2}} = \delta_1$ is often referred to as the domain wall thickness parameter.

Using the same values for $A$ and $K_1$ gives

$$\delta = \pi \left( \frac{2 \times 10^{-11}}{4 \cdot 7 \times 10^4} \right)^{\frac{1}{2}} = 6 \cdot 5 \times 10^{-8} \, \text{m} (= 6 \cdot 5 \times 10^{-6} \, \text{cm} = 650 \, \text{Å})$$

These values for wall energy and thickness compare reasonably well with what is found experimentally.

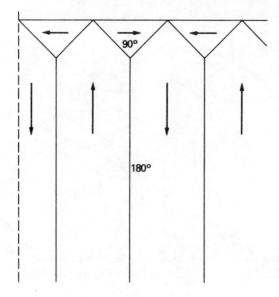

**Figure 6.5**   Domains of closure.

### 6.1.4   *Arrangements of domains*

The shape and size of the domains present in equilibrium in a
specimen are given by the condition that the total energy shall be a
minimum. They depend considerably on the actual configuration of the
specimen.

In a long, thin single crystal of iron cut with its surface accurately
parallel to a (100) crystal face, the domain boundaries are parallel lines
and the domains which they separate are alternately oppositely
magnetized in the direction of the lines. At the end surfaces domains of
closure are formed. These minimize the formation of 'free poles' and
reduce the magnetostatic energy. But extra domain boundaries need to
be created (Fig. 6.5).

When a field is applied to such a specimen along its length the
boundary walls move laterally so that those domains magnetized in
the same sense as the field grow wider and those oppositely magnetized
contract.

More complicated arrangements of domain walls are usually found in
practice. A possible arrangement in a single-crystal slab of iron
magnetized by the application of a field along a [110] direction is shown
in Fig. 6.6. When the surface of the specimen is very slightly

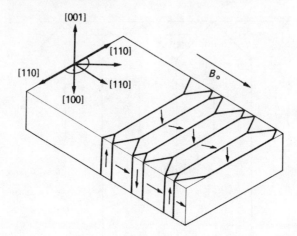

**Figure 6.6** Domain structure in a single crystal iron specimen having field and magnetization along a [110] direction. (After Stoner, 1950, *Rep. Prog. Phys.*, **13**, 114.)

inclined to a (100) face of an iron crystal, a 'fir-tree' pattern grows around the lines of the longitudinal domain boundaries (Fig. 6.7) and this gets more prominent as the inclination increases. The tree patterns are a kind of closure domain (Fig. 6.8).

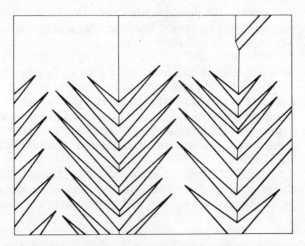

**Figure 6.7**   Tracing of a Bitter pattern showing fir-tree domains on the surface of an iron–silicon alloy single crystal cut nearly parallel to a (100) crystal face (times 500). (After Williams, Bozorth and Shockley, 1949, *Phys. Rev.*, **75**, 155.)

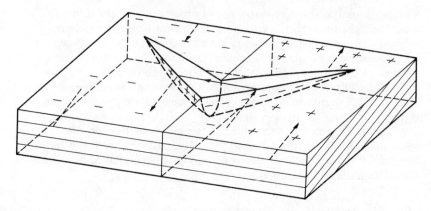

**Figure 6.8**    Interpretation of tree patterns. The lines on the side surface are traces of (100) planes. (After Stoner, 1950, *Rep. Prog. Phys.*, **13**, 114.)

### 6.1.5    *Experimental observation of magnetic domains*

The long-established method of looking at magnetic domains is that using Bitter patterns. Fine particles of a magnetic powder, usually in the form of a magnetic colloid, are spread on the surface of the specimen being examined. The surface must be carefully polished, usually electrolytically, and must be free from strains. The particles are attracted to regions of strong magnetic field gradient, usually where domain boundaries intersect the surface. Suitable magnetic colloids are easy to make, but the preparation of a suitably strain-free polished surface that characterizes the whole specimen is fairly difficult. The method has been used extensively for the study of static domain structures at room temperature. However, it is almost useless for dynamic studies of domain wall movements and it is difficult to use at temperatures far different from room temperature.

Another method of examination uses magneto-optical effects. This method has had wide application. Domains can be detected by their influence on the reflection of plane-polarized light incident on their surface. The magneto-optic Kerr effect is used. The polarization state of the reflected light depends on the magnitude and direction of the magnetization of the reflecting surface. Sensitive methods for the polarization analysis of the reflected light are required.

A similar application to transparent magnetic specimens uses the Faraday effect. The rotation of the plane of polarization of light transmitted through the specimen depends on the domain magnetization.

A suitable analysing microscope allows observation of the domain structure right through the volume of a thin transparent specimen.

These magneto-optical methods have the tremendous advantage of being available for dynamic studies of domain configurations, for instance in oscillatory applied fields of fairly high frequency.

A third method of domain examination uses transmission electron microscopy (Lorentz microscopy). The specimens are usually in the form of thin solid films not thicker than about 1000 Å. Electrons passing through the specimen feel the effect of the magnetic field gradients associated with the domain boundaries. The patterns produced in the detector by the transmitted electrons may be interpreted to give sensitive information about the domains.

### 6.1.6  Magnetoelastic energy and magnetostriction

The magnetostrictive effect is the change in dimensions which usually accompanies a change in the magnetization of a ferromagnetic single crystal. The magnetostriction coefficient $\lambda$ is the fractional change in length associated with a change in magnetization from zero to the saturation value.

Conversely, the effect of a unidirectional strain in the specimen is to introduce an additional anisotropy in the magnetization. In iron, for example, the effect of tension is to produce a tendency towards a preferred direction of magnetization parallel to the direction of the strain.

There is a close physical relationship between the magnetocrystalline anisotropy and the magnetostriction. Magnetostriction occurs because the magnetocrystalline anisotropy energy depends on the strain in such a way that the stable state of the crystal is deformed with respect to the original lattice. The crystal will deform spontaneously if to do so will lower the magnetocrystalline anisotropy energy.

Magnetoelastic energies can make an important contribution to the total magnetic energy of a ferromagnetic crystal which is strained, and so they can affect the domain properties very significantly. It is this aspect which most concerns us here. We simplify the treatment by assuming that the magnetoelastic effects act as though they give rise to an apparent contribution to the magnetocrystalline anisotropy of the crystal.

An isotropic magnetostriction coefficient $\lambda$ is defined, being some weighted mean of the directional coefficients (for cubic crystals) $\lambda_{100}$ and $\lambda_{111}$. The magnetoelastic contribution to the energy is then

$$E_{\text{me}} = \tfrac{3}{2} \lambda \tau \sin^2 \phi \qquad (6.19)$$

where $\tau$ is the tensile stress acting and $\phi$ is the angle between this stress and the direction of the magnetization.

The main effect for us here is that domain walls can encounter local energy barriers due to local stresses in the vicinity of imperfections in crystals.

### 6.1.7  Magnetization curves and domain wall equilibrium

When a 180° domain boundary wall of area $A$ moves laterally through a displacement $x$ a volume $Ax$ of the specimen reverses its magnetization, from $+M$ to $-M$. The associated change in magnetic energy per unit area of the wall is then $2(B_0)_i M x$, where $(B_0)_i$ is the internal field acting. If $E$ is the potential energy per unit area of the boundary (related to its existence but not necessarily localized in the boundary itself), the condition for equilibrium in a field $B_0$ is

$$\frac{d}{dx}(E - 2B_0 M x) = 0 \qquad (6.20)$$

$x$ is so defined that $x = 0$ at a position of equilibrium. That is,

$$2B_0 M = dE/dx \qquad (6.21)$$

It is expected that $E$ will be a randomly-varying function of position (Fig. 6.9) due to the effect of local strains and other crystal imperfections

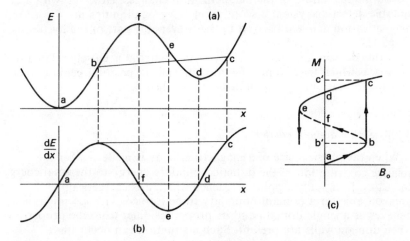

**Figure 6.9** Diagrams illustrating reversible and irreversible boundary movements. Corresponding points in parts (a), (b) and (c) are marked with the same letters. (After Stoner and Rhodes, 1949, *Phil. Mag.*, **40**, 481.)

on the boundary energy. As the field increases slowly, the boundary moves at first reversibly and the magnetization is a reversible function of the field. Eventually $dE/dx$ reaches a maximum value at b where the equilibrium becomes unstable. When the corresponding value of the field

$$(B_0)_{crit} = (dE/dx)_{max}/2M \tag{6.22}$$

has been passed the boundary moves spontaneously, with discontinuous and irreversible increase in magnetization, to a new position of equilibrium c having the same value of $dE/dx$. With further increase of field reversible movement of the boundary is resumed until a new maximum in $dE/dx$ is reached and further irreversible movement takes place. Eventually the field is large enough to sweep all boundaries through the specimen. Thereafter, in this particular example, the specimen is saturated. Otherwise when domains are present the magnetization of which does not lie in the field direction, the approach to saturation proceeds by a process of magnetization rotation.

If from position c in Fig. 6.9 the field is reduced the sign of the change in the magnetization energy in Equ. 6.20 is reversed and the discontinuous jump (in the reverse direction) cannot occur until the minimum in $dE/dx$ at e is reached. Thus hysteresis occurs in the graph of magnetization against field and the occurrence of the hysteresis loop (Fig. 1.1) is explained. For a macroscopic specimen the behaviour of many domain walls is superimposed, tending to smooth out the discontinuous nature of the magnetization changes. However, with a suitable detecting system discontinuous very small jumps in magnetization can be observed in the irreversible part of the hysteresis loop. This is the Barkhausen effect.

In this description, the coercivity of the material is closely related to the forces which tend to pin the domain walls in position, making them difficult to move under the influence of applied fields.


### 6.1.8    *Single-domain particles*

When the physical size of a magnetized body is made smaller the relative contribution of the domain boundary energy to the total energy increases. Eventually a point is reached where it is energetically unfavourable for a domain boundary to be formed. The specimen then behaves as a single domain and its properties differ from the properties when domain walls are present. Such a situation can occur in heterogeneous magnetic alloys in which fine particles of a ferromagnetic phase are dispersed within a non-ferromagnetic or a much less strongly ferromagnetic matrix.

To see what properties are expected to be associated with single domain particles we consider the simplest case, that of a single prolate ellipsoid, having directions of magnetization and applied field as shown in Fig. 6.10. Initially only magnetic anisotropy due to shape (magnetostatic energy) is considered, without magnetocrystalline and magnetoelastic effects. It turns out in the end that the effects left out can be treated in exactly the same way as shape anisotropy and they produce the same results.

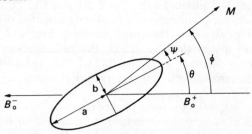

**Figure 6.10**   Definition of parameters for prolate ellipsoid in a magnetic field.

The general expression for the self-energy associated with the demagnetizing field (compare Equ. 6.6) of a general ellipsoid is

$$E_s = \tfrac{1}{2} M^2 (D_1 \alpha_1^2 + D_2 \alpha_2^2 + D_3 \alpha_3^2) \tag{6.23}$$

where $\alpha_1$, $\alpha_2$, $\alpha_3$, are the direction cosines of the magnetization $M$ with respect to the principal axes of the ellipsoid and $D_1$, $D_2$, $D_3$ are the demagnetization coefficients along these axes.

In the case considered here this becomes

$$E_s = \tfrac{1}{2} M^2 (D_a \cos^2 \psi + D_b \sin^2 \psi) \tag{6.24}$$

where $a$ and $b$ refer to the polar and equatorial axes respectively.

The energy associated with the field applied externally (see Equ. 6.5) is

$$E_{B_0} = -B_0 M \cos \phi \tag{6.25}$$

The total relevant energy is now

$$E' = E_s + E_{B_0} = \tfrac{1}{4}(D_b + D_a)M^2 - \tfrac{1}{4}(D_b - D_a)M^2 \cos 2\psi - B_0 M \cos \phi \tag{6.26}$$

Equ. 6.26 may be expressed in a dimensionless form

$$\eta' = \frac{E'}{(D_b - D_a)M^2} = \frac{(D_b + D_a)}{4(D_b - D_a)} - \frac{\cos 2\psi}{4} - \frac{B_0}{(D_b - D_a)M} \cos \phi \tag{6.27}$$

or, for the variable part of the energy

$$\eta = -\tfrac{1}{4} \cos 2\psi - b \cos \phi \tag{6.28}$$

$$= -\tfrac{1}{4} \cos 2(\phi - \theta) - b \cos \phi \tag{6.29}$$

where $b = B_0/(D_b - D_a)M$ is a reduced field. Treating $b$ and $\theta$ as fixed, the stationary (equilibrium) values of Equ. 6.29 are given by

$$\partial\eta/\partial\phi = \tfrac{1}{2}\sin 2(\phi - \theta) + b \sin \phi = 0 \qquad (6.30)$$

Solutions of Equ. 6.30 are required which give equilibrium values for $\cos \phi$ over a range of values for $b$ and at different values of the orientation angle $\theta$. $\cos \phi$ is really a reduced magnetization in the field direction while $b$ is the reduced field.

Graphs of solutions for different values of $\theta$ are given in Fig. 6.11. The combination of results for a collection of randomly oriented prolate ellipsoids of fixed ellipticity gives the graph shown in Fig. 6.12.

If the anisotropy of the particles is entirely due to shape the maximum reduced coercivity $b_c$ is where $b_c = 1$ (Fig. 6.11), for particles whose major axis lies in the same direction as the field. For randomly oriented particles $(b_c)_{ave} = 0.479$.

The upper limit of $(D_b - D_a)$ for long thin particles is $2\pi \times 10^{-7}$ SI units Thus the upper limit of coercivity due entirely to shape anisotropy in single domain particles is $(B_0)_c = 2\pi \times 10^{-7} MT$ ($H_c = 2\pi I$ Oe). This gives maximum coercive field values of about 1·1, 0·3, 0·9 T for iron, cobalt and nickel respectively (11 000, 3 000, 9 000 Oe).

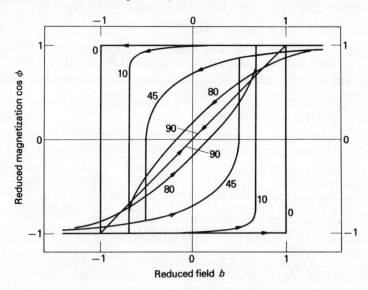

**Figure 6.11** Calculated magnetization curves for uniformly magnetized prolate ellipsoids. The numbers on the curves are the values in degrees of the angle $\theta$ between the polar axis and the field. (After Stoner and Wohlfarth, 1948, *Phil. Trans. R. Soc. A*, **240**, 599.)

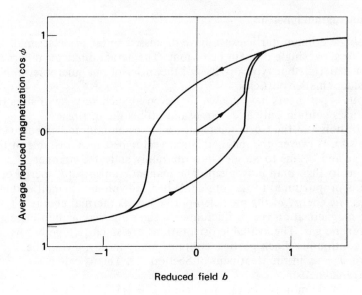

**Figure 6.12** Calculated magnetization curves for a collection of prolate ellipsoids of fixed ellipticity oriented at random. (After Stoner and Wohlfarth, 1948, *Phil. Trans. R. Soc.* A, **240**, 599.)

The basic treatment outlined here is for shape anisotropy. Exactly the same solution is obtained for spherical particles subject to stress. The difference lies in the definition of the reduced field, which becomes $b = B_0 M/3\lambda\tau$, where $\lambda$ is the effective magnetostriction coefficient and $\tau$ is the stress.

Magnetoelastic effects cannot account wholly for high values of coercivity in most materials because the possible values of the internal stress are too low.

The treatment is also the same for magnetocrystalline anisotropy, the reduced field becoming $b = B_0 M/2K_1$.

This leads to expected maximum coercivities due to magnetocrystalline anisotropy for iron, cobalt and nickel of about 0·05, 0·6 and 0·02 T (500, 6000 and 200 Oe).

Different mechanisms of domain magnetization are not really so clearly separable as might appear. In actual materials the boundaries between the regions of applicability of different mechanisms are diffuse. Often more than one mechanism operates at the same time. Such overlap would occur in a heterogeneous material containing particles of a range of sizes, some containing only one domain and others more than one.

## 6.2    Superparamagnetism

The single-domain particles we have discussed so far are just small
enough to show single domain behaviour. The actual diameter differs in
different materials but typically it is of the order of one micrometre. Now
we consider smaller particles.

Various experiments have shown that even at such very small sizes that
the particles contain only a few thousand atoms the intrinsic
magnetization and the Curie temperature are essentially independent of
particle size. However, the magnetization vector becomes unstable in this
size range and begins to wander in a thermally activated manner
analogous to Brownian movement. The magnetic anisotropy energy of a
particle is proportional to its volume. When the volume is small enough
the magnetic energy of the particle approaches its thermal energy $kT$,
and the magnetization vector fluctuates in the same way as in a classical
paramagnetic gas. The available orientations are so close together as to
appear continuous. Each particle contains many atoms, giving the
condition $J = \infty$ in the treatment of Section 2.3. This is called
superparamagnetism.

The magnetic moment of one particle is $\mu = MV$, where $V$ is its volume.
The apparent magnetization $M_a$ of an assembly of such particles in

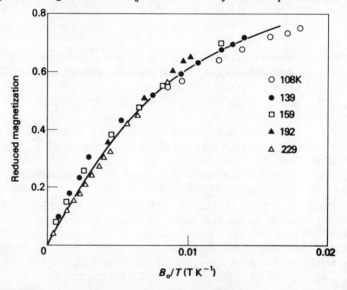

**Figure 6.13**  Superparamagnetic behaviour. Reduced magnetization for a finely divided ferrite
plotted against $B_0/T$ for several different temperatures. The line is calculated from the Brillouin
function with $J = \infty$ and fitted to the experimental data at one point.

thermal equilibrium at a temperature $T$ is given by adapting Equ. 2.6, giving

$$M_a/M = \coth(\mu B_0/kT) - kT/\mu B_0 \qquad (6.31)$$

One feature of Equ. 6.31 is that the apparent magnetization is determined universally by the ratio of field to temperature, $B_0/T$. This is found experimentally, as shown in Fig. 6.13. When $B_0/T$ is small, what seems to be true paramagnetic behaviour occurs and Equ. 6.31 can be approximated to its shortened form, as in Section 2.4. This gives

$$M_a/M = \mu B_0/3kT \qquad (6.32)$$

By use of Equ. 6.32 $\mu$ can be measured experimentally and hence the particle volume may be determined.

Since the apparent magnetization is zero when no external field is applied the coercivity associated with larger single-domain particles disappears. Thus a reduction in the size of highly-coercive single-domain particles eventually produces a fall in coercivity.

We have been discussing the condition of thermal equilibrium so far. In fact significant relaxation times $\tau$ sometimes occur when the superparamagnetic region is being approached, these decreasing rapidly as the magnetic energy approaches $kT$. This is illustrated in Table 6.2.

**Table 6.2** Relaxation times of single-domain particles.

| $\mu B_0/kT$ | $\tau$ (s) |
| --- | --- |
| 50 | $5 \times 10^{12}$ |
| 25 | $10^2$ |
| 18 | $10^{-1}$ |
| 10 | $2 \times 10^{-5}$ |
| 1 | $3 \times 10^{-9}$ |

## 6.3 Soft magnetic materials

Soft ferromagnetic or ferrimagnetic materials are those which have been developed with technical applications in view, to allow changes in magnetization to occur easily in weak fields. In this chapter we deal with the materials themselves, deferring a discussion of applications to Chapter 8. Different groups of materials exist according to the particular physical property that is being exploited.

The first group is that having the highest possible permeability, usually under static conditions; that is, where the change in induction $B$ produced by a small field $B_0$ is as large as possible. The problem here is to minimize the constraints on the mechanism by which change of overall magnetization takes place. One approach is to make pure single-crystal specimens that are chemically and structurally of a high degree of perfection. This has been possible in a few special cases, but it is not very attractive commercially. The other approach is to find materials the fundamental properties of which minimize the effect of imperfections on the magnetism.

In binary nickel–iron alloys the magnetocrystalline anisotropy constants $K_1$ and $K_2$ pass through zero near the composition of 75 at. % of nickel. There is a tendency to form a crystallographic superlattice at this composition and this must be suppressed by heat treatment of the specimens, otherwise the crossover composition is different. Low values of $K_1$ and $K_2$ (Section 6.1.3) lead to low domain wall energies, and easier wall motion. The magnetostriction coefficient $\lambda$ passes through zero at a rather higher concentration of nickel, and a low value of $\lambda$ is necessary to reduce the effect of internal stresses remaining in the specimen. Thus in selecting the best composition there has to be a compromise between these requirements. Various commercial alloys exist having different trade names where small amounts of third elements are added in order to optimize the properties. Maximum permeabilities of more than $10^5$ and coercivities as low as $2 \times 10^{-7}$ T $(2 \times 10^{-3}$ Oe$)$ have been achieved.

The second group of materials is for such applications as power transformers, generators and motors, with operating frequencies around 50 Hz. Losses of energy due to eddy currents become significant here. The principal requirements of the materials are to give high induction $B$ in moderate fields, coupled with acceptable energy losses. Pure iron is quite a good material in this group, but its properties are much improved by the addition of a few parts per cent (by weight) of silicon in solid solution.

An important effect of the dissolved silicon is to increase the electrical resistivity and so to reduce eddy currents. The other desirable effects are based mainly on metallurgical properties. The saturation magnetization of iron is reduced very little when the silicon is added. Silicon–iron is used in the form of thin polycrystalline sheets. With suitable combinations of rolling and heat treatments, grain-oriented sheets containing large (of the order of one centimetre) crystals can be made commercially. These have a (110) crystallographic plane in the plane of the sheet and a common [001] easy direction of magnetization in the direction of rolling, along the length of the sheet. This optimizes the permeability and reduces the coercivity. In use, the sheets are often built up into closed magnetic circuits with each limb made of easy-direction sheet. Coercivities are higher and maximum permeabilities are lower than for nickel–iron alloys, but maximum inductions are much higher and eddy current losses are smaller.

New problems arise when soft magnetic materials are required for use at high alternating frequencies. Generally non-metallic magnetic materials must be used. Such materials are ferrimagnetic rather than ferromagnetic, although the preceding discussion on domain properties in ferromagnets applies also to them. While all ferrites have electrical resistivities at least three orders of magnitude higher than those of metallic ferromagnets, there are wide variations between different ferrites. Their resistivities vary between $10^{-2}$ and $10^7$ $\Omega$ cm and those having relatively low values can produce energy losses due to eddy currents when used in high-frequency transformers. Other sources of energy loss at high frequencies are relaxation effects. Spins, either in pure rotation processes or in domain walls, react at a finite rate to oscillatory conditions. Energy is absorbed and the permeability deteriorates. There are also resonance effects which absorb energy.

Those ferrimagnetic oxides which have relatively high permeabilities commonly have coercivities of about $10^{-5}$ T ($10^{-1}$ Oe). Their energy losses are comparatively high and their use is limited to frequencies below 500 kHz.

High-frequency ferrites have relatively low permeabilities at low frequencies but they retain their properties at frequencies up to 10 MHz or more. Some materials of this general kind may be used up to microwave frequencies.

## 6.4  Hard magnetic materials

The technical requirement of hard magnetic materials is that they shall retain a high state of magnetization when the field which has produced the state is removed. In many applications the magnetization should also be as stable as possible with respect to time and to ambient temperature.

Thus a permanent magnet must have remanence which is as large as possible. The other important requirement is that its coercivity shall be high. A permanent magnet must necessarily possess an internal demagnetizing field $(B_0)_D$ the size of which depends on the geometry of the magnet. This is so whether the magnet is straight or whether it forms a nearly-closed loop. When no external field is applied the magnetization is set not by the remanence but by that value of the magnetization appropriate to a negative field of value $(B_0)_D$ (see Fig. 6.14). The reduction in overall magnetization compared with the remanent value is least when the demagnetizing field is a small proportion of the coercive field; that is, when the coercivity is greatest. Otherwise, when short fat

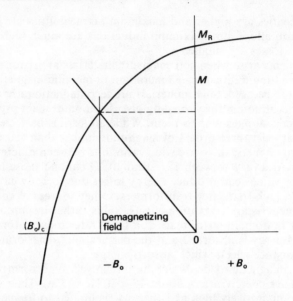

**Figure 6.14**  The working point of a permanent magnet.

permanent magnets are required that have large demagnetizing fields only materials of relatively high coercivity may be used.

In highly coercive materials a large amount of magnetostatic energy must be provided in order that the energy barriers, which pin down the domain walls or other mechanisms necessary for magnetization reversal, may be overcome.

One of the most widely used permanent magnet materials is barium ferrite $BaFe_{12}O_{19}$. This has a very large magnetocrystalline anisotropy. The easy direction of magnetization lies along the direction of the sixfold $c$-axis of the hexagonal crystal structure. Magnets are usually prepared by making use of oriented material. When the ferrite has been prepared having the correct chemical composition it is powdered to a controlled particle size. This must not be too small, or superparamagnetic behaviour will intervene and reduce the available coercivity. The powder is then oriented in a strong magnetic field, compacted and sintered by heating for an extended period at a temperature a little below 1300°C. In other applications the powder is oriented and dispersed within a matrix of a polymer which is then allowed to harden. The final composite magnet is often flexible.

The physical mechanism of magnetic hardness in barium ferrite is clearly dominated by the high magnetocrystalline anisotropy. In this, as in many other anisotropic uniaxial materials, it is energetically unfavourable for domains of closure to form near the end surfaces of the specimen.

Permanent magnet materials which use shape anisotropy as their basis are the elongated single-domain particle materials (ESD). Particles are produced which are small enough to give single-domain behaviour and which are sufficiently elongated to have high shape anisotropy and therefore high coercivity. In commercial materials of this kind the particles are usually of iron or iron–cobalt alloy. Again they are dispersed throughout a non-magnetic matrix, aligned in a magnetic field and then compacted into the required external form. While the single-domain theory outlined in Section 6.1.8 applies in principle to these materials it is too simple. Magnetostatic interactions between particles occur and these cause 'non-coherent' modes of magnetization reversal to occur. The coercivity is lower than that expected from the theory given in Section 6.1.8.

Alloys of iron, nickel and aluminium form the basis of a very widely used group of permanent magnet materials. There are usually small amounts of other additional elements present. These are heterogeneous alloys in which a ferromagnetic phase is precipitated metallurgically from a solid solution during a carefully controlled heat treatment. The metallurgical state of the alloys is complicated and the conditions for obtaining the best permanent magnet properties are critical. The mechanism for the production of the high coercivity is some compound of shape, strain and magnetocrystalline anisotropy effects in the magnetic particles precipitated from the non-ferromagnetic or more weakly ferromagnetic alloy matrix.

A remarkable new permanent magnetic material is the rare-earth intermetallic compound $SmCo_5$. The magnetocrystalline anisotropy of this compound is very high (see Section 6.1.1), and sintered specimens have very high coercivities. The exact mechanism of magnetization reversal in $SmCo_5$ is not yet understood in detail. However, it is thought to be some feature of the domain boundaries being unusually thin (as a result of the high value of the magnetocrystalline anisotropy), these being pinned in an extremely energetic way by macroscopic imperfections in the body of the material.

In general the theory of the coercivity of ferromagnets is not yet in a state which is quantitatively reliable. Because of the complicated nature of the mathematical problems it has not kept pace with experiment. Recent papers have indicated that a proper consideration of the inter-relation between domain wall thickness and the effective width and structure of the crystal imperfections and grain boundaries which impede wall motion is possible and is likely to succeed.

## 6.5   Thin magnetic films and bubble domains

There has been much experimental work on domain structures in very thin films of ferromagnetic materials, both single crystal and polycrystalline, and this has added greatly to the knowledge of domain behaviour. Also, iron whiskers have been studied in detail. These are minute crystals of iron having a high degree of structural perfection which are grown in a special way, such as the reduction of ferrous chloride by hydrogen. These studies have also given much new information on domain characteristics.

The particular case which concerns us here is that of a thin single-crystal film of a uniaxial ferromagnetic (or ferrimagnetic) material having its easy axis perpendicular to the plane of the film. Such a material might be one of the rare-earth garnets, grown with selected orientation by an epitaxial method from the vapour phase. A typical film thickness is about 20 $\mu$m ($2 \times 10^{-3}$ cm). In such a specimen the domain structure may be observed in transmitted light using the Faraday effect.

When the specimen is initially demagnetized it contains equal areas magnetized up and down. Applying a relatively small field perpendicular to the film causes the unfavoured domains to shrink (Fig. 6.15). When there is no marked anisotropy within the plane of the film the domain walls wander irregularly over the surface of the film (Fig. 6.16a). Applying a fixed field that is insufficient for saturation is observed to make the unfavoured domains thinner (Fig. 6.16b). When a stronger pulsed field of the same sign is superimposed on the steady field the negative domains start to break up into small cylindrical domains called bubbles which are then stable (Fig. 6.16c). Repeating the pulse produces more bubbles (Fig. 6.16d). The bubble domains are magnetic dipoles which mutually repel each other and which can be moved about the

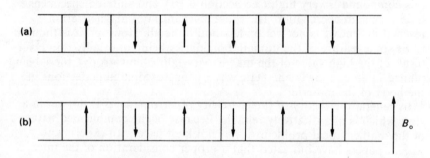

**Figure 6.15**   Domains in a uniaxial thin film magnetized at right angles to its plane: (a) without field; and (b) with field.

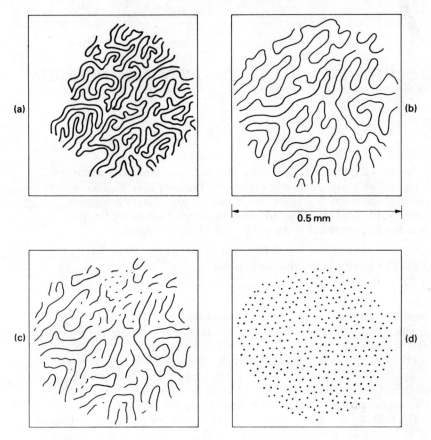

**Figure 6.16**   Formation of bubble domains: (a) in no field; (b) in a fixed small field; (c) after one superimposed pulse; and (d) after several pulses. (After O'Dell, 1974, *Magnetic Bubbles*, Macmillan.)

specimen by applying field gradients. Their diameter is of the order of a few micrometres.

Bubble domains have a large potential in device applications, particularly in computers. They can be guided through specimens on 'tracks' and made to take part in logic operations. A moving line of bubbles is equivalent to a moving recorder tape coated with magnetic oxide, but is much more versatile.

# 7

# Techniques of Magnetic Measurements

In this chapter we review some methods of obtaining experimental information about magnetic materials. The aim is to give an insight into the problems which arises when magnetic parameters are measured; into some ways in which these problems have been solved in the past; and into the limitations of some of the measuring methods.

## 7.1  The generation of magnetic fields

Magnetic fields are always generated by use of the magnetic effects of electric currents. Sometimes the effect of the current is indirect, being used to magnetize a permanent magnet which is then used independently. The problems in producing magnetic fields are usually one or more of the following:

(a) Making the field strong enough. The need is to optimize the magnetic effects of the electric current, and thus to concentrate the electrical energy into a volume as small as possible without creating intolerable problems from Joule heating by the current.

(b) Making the field sufficiently uniform over distance, or otherwise introducing some controlled spatial variation of the field such as a gradient.

(c) Making the field sufficiently stable over an acceptable period of time. If Joule heat is not removed adequately or its effects compensated, the temperature and thus the resistance of the wire carrying the current will vary with time.

It is often very difficult to solve all these problems at the same time.

### 7.1.1  Solenoid magnets with air cores

Most coil systems that are used to generate strong magnetic fields are composed of circular windings. The field produced by a system may be calculated by superposing the field contributions of all the separate turns. The unit in this calculation is a single circular current. In this section it is convenient to deal with the magnetic excitation $H$, measured in SI units as A m$^{-1}$. The field $B_0$ (in T) is given by $B_0 = \mu_0 H$. In CGS units $\mu_0 = 1$.

The value of $H$ along the axis of a single circular current at a distance $z$ from the plane of the current is

$$H_z = \frac{i\rho^2}{2(z^2 + \rho^2)^{3/2}} \qquad (7.1)$$

where $i$ is the current and $\rho$ is the radius of the current.

For points off the axis the calculation of the field is more complicated but it is straightforward and well documented. When a field is required that is homogeneous along the axis a system of two or more coaxial coils may be devised for which the derivative of the field at the central point is zero.

Practical solenoids are usually of finite thickness and length, often being made up of many turns of relatively thin wire wound uniformly within a rectangular winding cross section (Fig. 7.1).

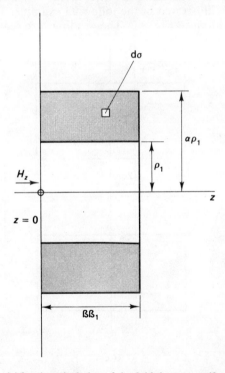

**Figure 7.1** Model for the calculation of the field due to a uniform solenoid.

If the wire is wound uniformly the current density $\tau$ is the same at any point within the winding space. The actual current at that point is $\tau\,d\sigma$. Taking the dimensional parameters as defined in Fig. 7.1, the value of $H$ at the origin is given by

where $F_1$ is a geometrical factor

$$H_z(0) = \tau\rho_1 F_1 \tag{7.2}$$

$$F_1 = \tfrac{1}{2}\beta \ln\left(\frac{\alpha + (\alpha^2 + \beta^2)^{\frac{1}{2}}}{1 + (1 + \beta^2)^{\frac{1}{2}}}\right) \tag{7.3}$$

Values of $F_1$ are easy to calculate, or they may be read from tables. Equivalent expressions may be used for the field gradient

$$H'_z(0) = \tau F_2 \tag{7.4}$$

where $F_2$ is similarly tabulated.

The procedure for estimating the field on the axis away from the centre of a coil is illustrated in the following example. The dimensions of the solenoid are given in Fig. 7.2. The windings are regular, there being

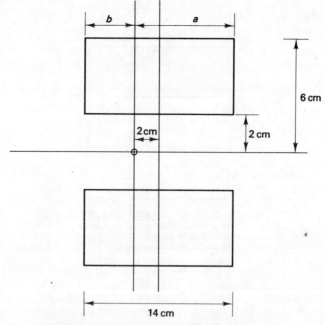

**Figure 7.2**   Dimensions of uniform solenoid.

five turns per centimetre in both the radial and the axial directions. That is, $\tau = 25 \times 10^4 i$ A m$^{-2}$.

From the diagram, $\rho_1 = 0.02$ m. For part a of the coil, $\alpha = 6/2 = 3$ and $\beta_a = 4.5$. For these parameters (Equ. 7.3) $F_1(\alpha,\beta_a) = 0.9106$. For part b of the coil, $\alpha = 3$ and $\beta_b = 2.5$, for which $F_1(\alpha,B_b) = 0.7824$. That is,

$$H_z = 0.02\,\tau\,(0.9106 + 0.7824) = 0.03386\tau = 8465i \text{ A m}^{-1}$$

This is equivalent to $B_0 = 1.064 \times 10^{-2}i$ T or $1.064 \times 10^2 i$ Oe.

This model is applicable to low-power conventional solenoids, and also to superconducting solenoids. In many cases the dissipation of large amounts of power is a serious problem, which is considered in Section 7.1.2.

One way of getting better cooling efficiency is to make a thick solenoid of single turns shaped out of copper sheets. The form of each turn, or pancake, is shown in Fig. 7.3.

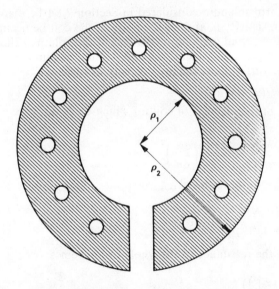

**Figure 7.3**    Single 'pancake' turn of Bitter solenoid.

Here the length of the current path is least in the centre and greatest on the outside, being proportional to the radius $\rho$. The effective resistance of the path is likewise proportional to the radius $\rho$. That is, since the ends of the turns are equipotential surfaces the current density is proportional to $\rho^{-1}$.

When a helix is made out of a collection of such pancakes by suitable cutting, stacking and joining together, a Bitter solenoid is produced.

The analytical treatment for this case is broadly similar to that for the uniform solenoid. $\tau_0$ is now the current density at the inner edge, so that

$$\tau = (\tau_0/\rho)\rho_1$$

The geometrical coefficients $K_1$ and $K_2$ are again tabulated, so that

$$H_z(0) = \tau_0\rho_1 K_1 \tag{7.5}$$

and

$$H'_z(0) = \tau_0 K_2 \tag{7.6}$$

and using the tables the calculation is the same as for the uniform solenoid.

### 7.1.2  Power consumption and dissipation in a solenoid

Let the uniform solenoid considered in Section 7.1.1 be made from wire having a resistivity $\eta$, and let the body of the coil be occupied to a fraction $\lambda$ by the actual conductor, the rest of the volume being used as insulation, interspaces between turns and cooling medium. The whole coil contains $N$ turns. Thus the area density of turns is

$$dN/d\sigma = N/(\alpha-1)\beta\rho_1^2 \tag{7.7}$$

The resistance of the element of coil for which $d\sigma$ is the cross sectional area is

$$dR = \frac{2\pi\rho\eta dN}{\lambda(d\sigma/dN)} = \frac{2\pi\rho\eta}{\lambda}\left(\frac{dN}{d\sigma}\right)^2 d\sigma, \tag{7.8}$$

or, putting $d\sigma = d\rho\, dz$ we have

$$dR = \frac{2\pi\eta N^2}{\lambda(\alpha-1)^2\beta^2\rho_1^4}\, \rho\, d\rho\, dz \tag{7.9}$$

By integration the resistance of the whole coil becomes

$$R = \frac{\pi\eta N^2(\alpha+1)}{\lambda\beta\rho_1(\alpha-1)} \tag{7.10}$$

The current density is given by

$$\tau = \frac{iN}{(\alpha-1)\beta\rho_1^2} \tag{7.11}$$

where $i$ is the current.

If the steady-state power consumption is $W = i^2R$, we have

$$\tau = \frac{1}{\rho_1}\left(\frac{W\lambda}{\eta\rho_1}\right)^{\frac{1}{2}}\left(\frac{1}{\pi\beta(\alpha^2-1)}\right)^{\frac{1}{2}} \tag{7.12}$$

This value for $\tau$ may now be substituted in Equ. 7.2 to give

$$H_z(0) = \left(\frac{W\lambda}{\eta\rho_1}\right)^{\frac{1}{2}} G_1 \tag{7.13}$$

where $G_1$ is a wholly geometrical factor given by

$$G_1 = \left(\frac{1}{\pi\beta(\alpha^2-1)}\right)^{\frac{1}{2}} F_1 \tag{7.14}$$

Values of $G_1$ for different $\alpha$ and $\beta$ are available in tabulated form.

Obtaining the highest possible field for a given expenditure of power (and thus of cooling capacity) is then a question of finding the shape of the coil having the highest value of $G_1$. For a uniform solenoid of the kind considered $(G_1)_{max} = 0.142$, and this occurs for that shape for which $\alpha = 3$ and $\beta$ goes from $-2$ to $+2$. The highest $G_1$ for a Bitter coil is $0.166$ (17% improvement) and another such single-turn solenoid using pancake turns of variable thickness gives $(G_1)_{max} = 0.185$ (30% improvement on a uniform solenoid).

It is instructive to calculate the order of maximum field that might be expected from a given solenoid. Consider a Bitter solenoid of optimum shape, so that $G_1 = 0.166$, having an internal radius (which controls the size of the working space available in the field being produced) of 3 cm. The packing factor $\lambda = 0.5$ and the maximum power $W$ available is 1 MW. Let the pancakes be made of copper of resistivity $\eta = 2 \times 10^{-8}$ $\Omega$m. Then the largest value of $H$ available is

$$H_z(0) = G_1(W\lambda/\eta\rho_1)^{\frac{1}{2}} = 4.79 \times 10^6 \text{ A m}^{-1}$$

The equivalent field is $B_0 = \mu_0 H = 6.0$ T (or 60 kOe).

If the temperature of the conducting material rises as a result of Joule heating field stability with respect to time is lost, unless electronic stabilization of the current is used. When the current density exceeds $3 \times 10^6$ A m$^{-2}$ (300 A cm$^{-2}$) a cooling device is usually built into the solenoid. This has the effect of reducing the packing factor $\lambda$. For conventional solenoids which are non-superconducting and have no ferromagnetic core, cooling methods are listed in Table 7.1.

**Table 7.1**   Types of cooling for solenoids.

| Field | tesla | oersted | Method of cooling |
|---|---|---|---|
| Up to about | $10^{-2}$ | $10^2$ | Natural convection |
| | $10^{-1}$ | $10^3$ | Cooling plates inserted within the coils |
| | 1 | $10^4$ | Conductors in the form of tubes with coolant flowing inside |
| | 10 | $10^5$ | Axial coolant flow through tubes in Bitter-type coils |

### 7.1.3  Mechanical effects in solenoids

The current in the windings of a solenoid reacts mechanically with the field and when the field is strong the forces are very appreciable. The equivalent stress on the outermost turns of wire can well exceed the tensile strength of copper wire, causing failure (which might be explosive) if the turns are unsupported. Special construction is often employed to avoid this, and windings of higher tensile strength are sometimes used.

Considerable amounts of energy are stored in energized magnets. The magnetic energy per unit volume is $\frac{1}{2} HB$. For a field of 10 T ($10^5$ Oe), equivalent to $H = 7.96 \times 10^6$ A m$^{-1}$, the potential energy is $3.98 \times 10^7$ J m$^{-3}$. (For comparison the explosive power of TNT is about $6 \times 10^9$ J m$^{-3}$).

In all energized magnet systems a safety device, often a high-impedance resistive load connected in parallel, is inserted into the power supply, so that in the event of sudden interruption of the current the magnetic energy can be dissipated relatively slowly.

### 7.1.4  Superconducting solenoids

If the solenoid is wound from wire made from a hard superconductor most of the problems to do with the dissipation of Joule heat are avoided. This leads to what is perhaps the simplest method of producing fairly large fields, so long as the required field stability is not great.

Fundamental properties of superconductors define their eligibility as materials for making solenoid magnets. Each material has a critical temperature above which it becomes normal. The critical temperatures of viable hard superconductors are between 10 K and 20 K, limiting the operating temperature to about 4 K or lower. At a chosen operating temperature there is a critical magnetic field above which the wire becomes normally conducting. This is greater than 10 T (100 kOe) for many materials that are commercially available. For given conditions of field and temperature there is a current density above which the normal state is reached. Critical current densities are typically about $10^9$ A m$^{-2}$ ($10^5$ A cm$^{-2}$).

The hardest known superconductor at the present time is the alloy $Nb_3Sn$. It has very poor mechanical strength. Other alloys that are used are NbZr, NbTi and $V_3Ga$. The design of superconducting magnets is often complicated by the inner turns seeing a higher field than those on the outside. The current tends to go critical selectively according to position within the coil. Composite construction is sometimes used to allow for this. A higher current density can be tolerated on the outside of the coil, or a material having a higher critical field may be used on the inside.

If a superconducting solenoid is working near its limit and it goes normal suddenly a large amount of stored energy is released and a violent explosion will occur if precautions are not taken. The stored magnetic energy could be augmented by that from a consequent rapid and violent evaporation of liquid helium from the cooling bath.

It is common to clad superconducting wire with a coating of a low-resistance normal conductor. If the superconductor goes normal a (reduced) current is carried locally by the cladding, increasing the time constant of the breakdown. In the most modern applications the superconductor is drawn down into very fine filaments within a copper matrix, the resistance of which is high compared with that of the superconductor. The mechanical properties of the whole wire are much improved and flux jumps and other instabilities tend to disappear. A typical commercial superconducting magnet made from filamentary NbTi will produce fields of about 8 T (80 kOe) when operated at a temperature of 4·2 K and just over 10 T (100 kOe) at 2·2 K.

### 7.1.5  Iron-cored electromagnets

Iron-cored electromagnets are often used when moderate field strengths are required. The power requirements are usually quite modest, and good control of spatial and time variation of the field can be obtained fairly easily.

In a closed magnetic circuit, such as the path indicated by the broken line in Fig. 7.4, we may write

$$i = \oint \boldsymbol{H}.\mathrm{d}\boldsymbol{l} \tag{7.15}$$

where $i$ is the total current looping the magnetic circuit, found by multiplying the number of turns of wire by the current in each. The quantity $\oint \boldsymbol{H}.\mathrm{d}\boldsymbol{l}$ is known as the magnetomotive force (MMF), by analogy

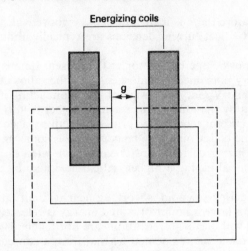

**Figure 7.4**  Layout of electromagnet.

with the electrical circuit where $\oint \boldsymbol{E}.d\boldsymbol{l}$ is called the electromotive force. In the same circuit the sum $\Sigma(l/\mu_r A)$ is called the reluctance, analogous to electrical resistance. The quantities $l$, $\mu_r$ and $A$ refer respectively to the length, relative permeability and area of cross section of each component in the magnetic path. We may now write for the total flux in the circuit

$$\Phi = \frac{\text{MMF}}{\text{reluctance}} \tag{7.16}$$

The flux at a point is given by $\Phi = BA$, where $B$ is the induction (that is, flux density). Also, $B = \mu_r\mu_0 H = \mu_r B_0$, so that $\Phi = \mu_r B_0 A$. Thus, in a magnetic circuit of constant area of cross section having a length $l$ of iron and $g$ comprising an air gap the field is given by

$$B_0 = \frac{i}{(l/\mu_r A) + g} \tag{7.17}$$

When the permeability of the iron $\mu_r$ is very much greater than unity (usually it is of the order of $10^4$) it is the length of the air gap which dominates the performance of the magnet. The design is complicated by the permeability of iron being variable with the field and by there being leakage effects.

Pole tips (Fig. 7.5) are often introduced, adjacent to the air gap, in order to concentrate the flux and so to increase the field. These are often truncated cones with an optimum cone semi-angle of just under 60°. For the largest fields the saturation magnetization of the pole tips should be

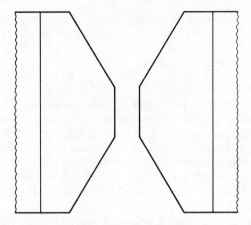

**Figure 7.5**   Conical pole tips.

as large as possible. In this case an iron–cobalt alloy having a high saturation magnetization is used, but this material is difficult to demagnetize. Often a versatile and stable performance is more important than the highest possible field and pole tips of soft iron are usually used.

The maximum effect from the ferromagnetic core of the magnet is achieved when the pole tips are saturated. There is no gain in making the magnet bigger beyond this point, except to provide better field uniformity or a larger working volume.

In most electromagnets the energizing coils are placed near to the pole gap and they contribute directly to the field, their direct contribution being often at least equal to that coming from the iron core. A point is reached eventually when the use of the iron core ceases to be worthwhile. The space occupied by the iron is better filled with turns of the conductor.

Some electromagnets employ a field-stabilizing device in the form of a Hall effect probe placed in the field, the output from which is processed and fed back to the circuit energizing the magnet, thereby controlling it. Stabilities of the order of 1 part in $10^6$ are possible in this way, in fields of about 1 T (10 kOe).

### 7.1.6   Pulsed magnetic fields

The limits for obtaining strong magnetic fields using non-superconducting magnets (superconducting magnets have different limitations) are mechanical strength and the dissipation of Joule heat. If field pulses of short duration are used the Joule heat need not be removed. It may be stored acceptably within the thermal capacity of the coil. The usable length of pulse $(t_m - t_0)$ is limited by the relationship

$$\int_{t_0}^{t} \eta(T)[\tau(t)]^2 \, dt < \int_{T_0}^{T_1} c(T) \, dT \tag{7.18}$$

The current density $\tau(t)$ and the specific heat capacity $c(T)$ refer to unit volume of the coil material. The resistance $\eta(T)$ is usually a fairly simple function of the temperature $T$. $T_0$ is the starting temperature of the coil. There are obvious benefits in making $T_0$ as low as possible. $T_1$ is the highest tolerable final temperature. It is set by the degree of damage which can be accepted in the coil. In the limit $T_1$ is the melting temperature of the wire or the temperature at which its insulation breaks down.

The method is to start with a source of stored energy (called the tank) such as a capacitor, a battery bank or a rotating dynamo. Let the available energy be $E_t$. During the pulse operation part of this energy is used in setting up the field and part is lost in Joule heat:

$$E_t = \int_{t_0}^{t_m} Ri^2 \, dt + \int_{t_0}^{t_m} (d\Phi/dt)i \, dt \tag{7.19}$$

The flux is given by $\Phi = Li$, where $L$ is the inductance of the coil. That is,

$$E_t = \int_{t_0}^{t_m} Ri^2 \, dt + \int_{0}^{t_m} Li \, di + \int_{t_0}^{t_m} (dL/dt)i^2 \, dt \tag{7.20}$$

In most cases a situation is aimed for in which the coil is rigid and where the current distribution within it does not change with time during the pulse. That is, where the third term in Equ. 7.20 is zero because $dL/dt = 0$. The second term in Equ. 7.20 is the useful magnetic energy $E_m$, equal to $\frac{1}{2} Li_m^2$, where $i_m$ is the maximum current in the pulse.

The efficiency $\kappa$ of the pulse operation is $E_m/E_t$. This is made less favourable when the third term of Equ. 7.20 is not zero but positive. This usually happens to some extent because the coil stretches somewhat as a result of the very large mechanical forces acting on it. There is also a tendency to push the current outwards within the conductor. Both effects tend to make $dL/dt$ positive.

The field produced at the centre of the coil is given very roughly by

$$B_0 = S(E_m \mu_0/V)^{\frac{1}{2}} \tag{7.21}$$

$V$ is the effective volume of the coil and $S$ is a geometrical factor depending on the shape of the coil. Its value is best, approaching unity, when the coil is long and narrow. $E_m$ is often of the order of 5000 J. Fields of the order of 50 T (500 kOe) have been produced in pulses about $10^{-3}$ s long.

Explosive pulse methods can be used to obtain still higher field strengths. If $dL/dt$ can be made large and negative by shrinking the coil explosively during the current pulse (see Equ. 7.20) a large magnification of the field is possible. As an example, in one experiment a coil made of 10 swg copper wire wound with 3 turns per inch was capable of producing a pulsed field of 9 T when used in a particular circuit. When it was explosively compressed to about one tenth of its original diameter within the 10 $\mu$s duration of the electrical pulse, fields of the order of 1400 T $(14 \times 10^6$ Oe) were produced over a sphere of about 6 mm diameter, lasting for the order of microseconds. This is of limited application since it is fairly difficult to complete many measurements reliably during such short measuring times, and not many physical properties are immune from being perturbed by the pressures involved.

## 7.2  Measurement of magnetic field

First we consider the measurement of field in free space or in air. The induction $B$ is given by

$$B = \mu_r B_0 = \mu_r \mu_0 H \tag{7.22}$$

$\mu_r$ is the relative permeability of the medium and this is very nearly unity for air. The flux $\Phi$ crossing an area $A$ is

$$\Phi = B A \tag{7.23}$$

Thus measurement of the flux leads to a knowledge of the field.

### 7.2.1  *Measurement of magnetic flux*

Let a search coil of area $A$ be placed in a magnetic field, so that a flux $\Phi$ is enclosed. When the flux is changed by switching off the field, by removing the coil or by turning the coil so that it encloses no flux, an EMF is produced across the ends of the coil which is related to the change in flux:

$$e = -\sum d\Phi/dt, \text{ or } \sum \Phi = B A = -\int_0^t e \, dt \tag{7.24}$$

An integrating device is required, to measure $\int e \, dt$ over the time of the flux change. This may be one of the following:

F

(a)  a ballistic galvanometer;
(b)  a moving coil fluxmeter;
(c)  an electronic integrator (there are various kinds); or
(d)  a rotating coil device.

## 7.2.2  Ballistic galvanometer

This is simply a moving-coil galvanometer having a time of oscillation long compared with the duration of the current pulse, the time integral of which is being measured.

Consider a galvanometer coil of $n$ turns and area $a$, situated in a radial magnetic field within the instrument. $i$ is the instantaneous current. The couple acting instantaneously on the coil (independent of the angle of rotation $\theta$) is $nahi$. The impulse of angular momentum is

$$\int_0^{t_1} nahi \, dt = nah \int i \, dt \tag{7.25}$$

This imparts an initial angular velocity of the coil, of value $(d\theta/dt)_0 = \theta'_0$, so that

$$I \theta'_0 = nah \int i \, dt = (nah/R) \int e \, dt \tag{7.26}$$

where $I$ is the moment of inertia of the moving coil and $R$ is the resistance of the coil circuit. For times later than $t = 0$,

$$I \theta'' + b \theta' + c \theta = 0$$

If $b$ is small (weak damping) the solution is of the form

$$\theta = \left[ \frac{nah}{I\omega} \exp \left( \frac{-bt}{2I} \right) \sin \omega t \right] \left( \frac{1}{R} \int e \, dt \right) \tag{7.27}$$

or, if $\theta_1$ is the first amplitude of oscillation

$$\int e \, dt = \theta_1 (\tau/2\pi)(c/nah)(1 + \lambda/4) \tag{7.28}$$

$c$, $\tau = 2\pi\omega$ and $\lambda$ are respectively the torsion constant of the suspension, the periodic time and the logarithmic decrement of the oscillation.

The instrument requires calibration. This may be done by measuring its deflection when a known impulse is imposed on it by reversal of a measured current through a standard mutual inductance. There are other equivalent methods of calibration. Flux may then be measured by connecting a search coil of known area to the instrument and manipulating it in the field. The accuracy of the flux measured in this way can be much better than $\pm 1\%$.

### 7.2.3   Fluxmeter

A moving coil fluxmeter is a galvanometer with the torque of its suspension so small as to be ineffective. There is strong electromagnetic damping, the coefficient of which is

$$b' = (nah)^2/R$$

Air damping of the coil is usually negligible. Now we write

$$I\,\theta'' + [(nah)^2/R]\,\theta' = nahi \tag{7.29}$$

If $L$ is the self-inductance of the search coil that is connected to the moving coil,

$$iR = -d\Phi/dt - Ldi/dt$$

That is,

$$I\,\theta'' + [(nah)^2/R]\theta' = (nah/R)(d\Phi/dt + Ldi/dt) \tag{7.30}$$

Angular momentum is imparted to the moving coil and electromagnetic damping stops the movement. Integrating Equ. 7.30 and noting that at the beginning and end of the process $\theta'$ and $i$ are both zero, we obtain

$$I[\theta']_0^0 + [(nah)^2/R]\,[\theta]_0^{\theta_1} = (nah/R)(\Phi_2 - \Phi_1) \tag{7.31}$$

or

$$\theta_1 = K' \Delta\Phi = K \int e\,dt \tag{7.32}$$

The calibration of the instrument is independent of the suspension and since all the dimensions are fixed it remains constant. Instrument makers usually supply a fixed calibration. Mostly, the resistance of the search coil has little effect. Drift of the zero reading of the instrument and also thermal EMF's can sometimes be troublesome and they need devices to control them.

Oscillatory field pulses cannot be measured in this way. The combination of search coil and fluxmeter can be seen as a flux-conserving system. The flux collected in the search coil transfers itself to the moving coil.

### 7.2.4   Electronic integrators

These do electronically exactly what has just been considered using electromagnetic–mechanical methods. A DC coupled amplifier is used which has a differentiating element in a feedback loop (Fig. 7.6).

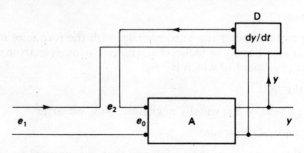

**Figure 7.6** Electronic integrator.

Let the output be $y = A e_0$, $e_2 = D \, dy/dt$ and $e_0 = e_1 + e_2$. That is,

$$y = A e_1 + A D \, dy/dt \tag{7.33}$$

Re-arranging and integrating with respect to time gives

$$y = -(1/D) \int e_1 \, dt + (1/AD) \int y \, dt \tag{7.34}$$

The second term in Equ. 7.34 is an error term which is ideally to be made as small as possible by having large amplification $A$. If long times of integration are required (say, for example $10^3$ s) the product $AD$ must be large (of the order of $10^6$).

One form of this is the Cioffi integrator (Fig. 7.7), although in its original form it did not actually use electronic parts. It used a galvanometer amplifier, with a mutual inductance as the differentiating device. A galvanometer amplifier consists of a primary galvanometer, the

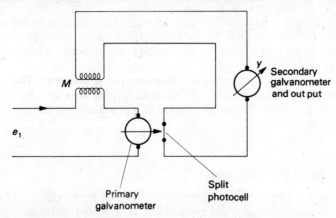

**Figure 7.7** Cioffi integrator using galvanometer amplifier.

light spot from which falls on a split photocell. The unbalanced output from the photocell is read on a secondary galvanometer. In this case $e_2 = M \, dy/dt$ and $y = (1/M) \int e \, dt$.

### 7.2.5  Rotating-coil devices

When a search coil is rotated in a field about an axis in its own plane (Fig. 7.8) it encloses a variable flux $\Phi = A \, B_z \sin \omega t$. $B_z$ is the component of induction perpendicular to the axis of rotation. An alternating EMF is induced in the coil having amplitude $A \, B_z \omega$ and this is used to measure $B_z$.

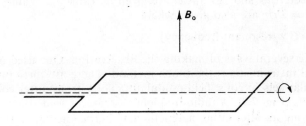

**Figure 7.8**  Rotating search coil.

The speed of rotation must be well controlled. Commercial instruments commonly have a second coil driven at the same speed on the same shaft, situated in a standard reference field. The field under investigation is then measured as a ratio with the standard field. The rotating coil can be made as small as a few millimetres in diameter.

Most search coil measurements are subject to second-order errors in field gradients. Special search coils (one is called a flux ball) have been designed so as to minimize these errors.

### 7.2.6  Nuclear magnetic resonance

Nuclear magnetic resonance in magnetic materials is mentioned from an intrinsic viewpoint in Section 5.2.2. Here we discuss its use to measure magnetic fields. The quantized energy levels of some nuclei in a magnetic field can be excited by high-frequency radiation and the frequency of resonance may be used as a particularly sensitive and accurate measure of the field strength. At resonance

$$\omega_0 = 2\pi f_0 = \pm \gamma B_0 \tag{7.35}$$

where $\gamma$ is the gyromagnetic ratio for the nucleus used. Values of $\gamma$ for

**Table 7.2** Gyromagnetic ratios and conversion factors between resonant frequency and field.

| Nucleus | $\gamma$ | | $G$ | |
|---|---|---|---|---|
| | $T^{-1}s^{-1}$ | $Oe^{-1}s^{-1}$ | $T\,s$ | $Oe\,s$ |
| $^1$H (proton) | $2{\cdot}6753 \times 10^8$ | $2{\cdot}6753 \times 10^4$ | $2{\cdot}3486 \times 10^{-8}$ | $2{\cdot}3486 \times 10^{-4}$ |
| $^2$D (deuteron) | $4{\cdot}1064 \times 10^7$ | $4{\cdot}1064 \times 10^3$ | $1{\cdot}5301 \times 10^{-7}$ | $1{\cdot}5301 \times 10^{-3}$ |
| $^7$Li | $1{\cdot}0396 \times 10^8$ | $1{\cdot}0396 \times 10^4$ | $6{\cdot}0438 \times 10^{-8}$ | $6{\cdot}0438 \times 10^{-4}$ |
| electron (DPPH) | $1{\cdot}762 \times 10^{11}$ | $1{\cdot}762 \times 10^7$ | $3{\cdot}566 \times 10^{-11}$ | $3{\cdot}566 \times 10^{-7}$ |

Frequency is measured in Hz.

protons, deuterons and $^7$Li nuclei are given in Table 7.2. Values of the quantity $G = 2\pi/\gamma$ are also given, where

$$\text{field} = G \times (\text{resonant frequency}) \tag{7.36}$$

There are several ways of making the observation. One used in some commercial instruments is the Bloch method. There are three mutually perpendicular sets of coils, field-modulating coils, transmitter coils and receiver coils (Fig. 7.9). A radio-frequency generator feeds the transmitter coils, applying an alternating magnetic field perpendicular to the field

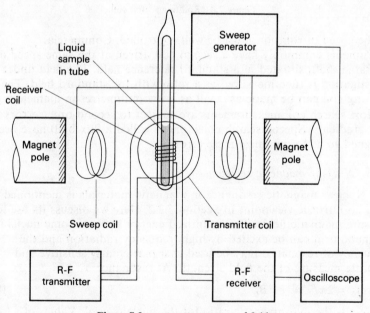

**Figure 7.9** NMR measurement of field.

being measured. The nuclei being excited are contained in a sample tube within the coil system. If the nuclei are protons the sample is water. At resonance the sample radiates to the receiver coils, the signal from which is displayed. The coils are adjusted initially so as to minimize direct signal transfer from transmitter to receiver. A sweep device modulates the main field over a small amplitude about its steady value in order that the resonance condition may be recognized more easily.

The radio-frequency signal is varied in frequency until resonance is found and then its frequency is measured. In accurate work an external crystal-controlled counter is used to measure the resonant frequency, and this may be calibrated against broadcast frequency standards. In the United Kingdom a very accurate standard is broadcast at a frequency of 200 kHz.

This method can be very sensitive. Under the most sensitive conditions the author has used it to detect changes of $2 \times 10^{-7}$ T (0·002 Oe) in a field of 0·8 T (8 kOe). This is a sensitivity of one part in $4 \times 10^{6}$. The resonance condition is difficult to detect if the field is not very uniform. The smallest probes are about 5 mm in diameter and the field variation should not exceed $10^{-4}$ T (1 Oe) over this diameter.

A variation of the same method is to use electron spin resonance (ESR) instead of NMR. The value of $\gamma$ for a free electron is several hundred times greater than that for a proton (see Table 7.2). Thus much weaker fields may be measured for the same resonant frequencies. A suitable material in which ESR may be observed is diphenyl picryl hydrazyl (DPPH). This is notable for its very sharp resonance. Values of the quantities $\gamma$ and $G$ for electrons are included in Table 7.2.

### 7.2.7   The Hall effect

When an electric current is passed through a conducting material placed in a magnetic field, in a direction perpendicular to the field, a Lorentz force acts on the conduction carriers which produces an EMF in the third perpendicular direction. This is the Hall effect. The EMF depends linearly on the field and can be used as a very convenient measure of field.

Various semiconducting compounds, such as InAs or InSb, are good materials for probes, but their sensitivity depends rather sharply on temperature. Careful control of temperature or electronic temperature compensation is necessary for accurate work.

### 7.2.8   Magnetoresistance

The electrical resistivity of conducting and semiconducting solids

increases when a magnetic field is applied. This is called
magnetoresistance and it may be used to measure field. The effect is not
linear in field. In the most sensitive materials (a eutectic compound of
InSb and NiSb is very sensitive) the influence of temperature is rather
large. This gives a convenient but not very accurate measure of field. The
main advantage is the very small field probes which are possible. One
appplication is in making detectors for reading out information from
magnetic bubble arrays.

### 7.2.9   *The measurement of pulsed fields*

Pulsed fields may be measured by using a search coil placed in a fixed
position in the field. The instantaneous EMF produced across the search
coil is $e(t) \propto dB_0/dt$, and thus the field is proportional to the time
integral of $e(t)$. An electronic integrator may therefore be used to
estimate the field. Since the exact output depends on the shape of the
pulse and other factors it is necessary to calibrate the measurement *in
situ* with reference to some known phenomenon within the field range
being covered.

### 7.2.10   *Field measurement within a magnetized body—the magnetic potentiometer*

It is often necessary to measure the field $(B_0)_i$ present inside a
ferromagnetic body when a demagnetizing field is acting. When the
demagnetizing field is relatively large and perhaps impossible to estimate
accurately, this is especially important. The magnetic potentiometer
(sometimes called the Chattock potentiometer) is useful for doing this.

The device consists of a coil, long compared with its diameter, wound
on to a non-magnetic core. The core is bent, typically into a semicircle
so that the ends of the coil lie in the same plane. The electrical ends of
the coil must be taken from the same physical point. The coil diameter
might be as small as 2 mm and the core diameter 15 mm, with about 100
turns of fine wire. The ends of the coil must lie flat on the ferromagnetic
surface (Fig. 7.10).

At any point the vector $H$ and the magnetic scalar potential $U$ are
related by

$$H = -\nabla U \tag{7.37}$$

The difference in potential between two points A and B (Fig. 7.10) is
thus

$$U_A - U_B = \int_{\text{line}} H.dl \tag{7.38}$$

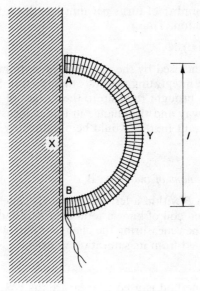

**Figure 7.10**   The magnetic potentiometer.

If the closed path from A back to A *via* B, taking path X outwards through the specimen and returning along path Y outside, encloses no electric current

$$\oint \boldsymbol{H}.\mathrm{d}\boldsymbol{l} = 0$$

Thus

$$\int_X \boldsymbol{H}.\mathrm{d}\boldsymbol{l} = \int_Y \boldsymbol{H}.\mathrm{d}\boldsymbol{l} \tag{7.39}$$

When A and B are close together we can write for the inside path

$$\int_X \boldsymbol{H}.\mathrm{d}\boldsymbol{l} = H_i l$$

where $H_i = (B_0)_i/\mu_0$, and $(B_0)_i$, is the internal field in the specimen.
For the path Y we consider the flux enclosed by the coil. This is

$$\mathrm{d}\Phi = \int \alpha \boldsymbol{B}_0.\mathrm{d}\boldsymbol{l}\, n = \mu_0 n \alpha \int_Y \boldsymbol{H}.\mathrm{d}\boldsymbol{l} \tag{7.40}$$

where $n$ is the number of turns per unit length on the coil and $\alpha$ is its area of cross section. Thus

$$(B_0)_i = (1/n\alpha l)\,d\Phi \qquad\qquad (7.41)$$

The flux $d\Phi$ enclosed by the magnetic potentiometer may be measured using one of the integrating methods described in Section 7.2.1. The potentiometer is brought right up to the surface of the specimen from a large distance away and the change in flux is measured. Usually the calibrating constant $(n\alpha l)^{-1}$ would be obtained by measurement in a known field.

### 7.2.11   *Measurement of induction* B

The induction $B$ within a ferromagnetic specimen may be measured by wrapping a search coil of known total area $A$ round the specimen (Fig. 7.11) and then measuring the change in flux when $B$ is changed. When $B$ is reversed from its saturation value $B_s$

$$\Delta\Phi = 2\,A\,B_s \qquad\qquad (7.42)$$

An integrating method is used to measure the change in flux. The search coil is often a few turns of insulated fine wire wound closely on to the specimen as a core.

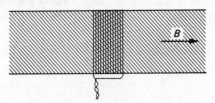

**Figure 7.11**   Measurement of induction $B$.

## 7.3   Measurement of magnetization

The magnetization of ferromagnetic specimens may be measured in three main ways. These are the induction method; the force method; and methods based on the detection of the dipole field of a magnetized specimen.

### 7.3.1   *The induction method*

If a magnetic dipole initially placed at the centre of a pick-up coil system is removed to a large distance a voltage $e$ is induced in the coil

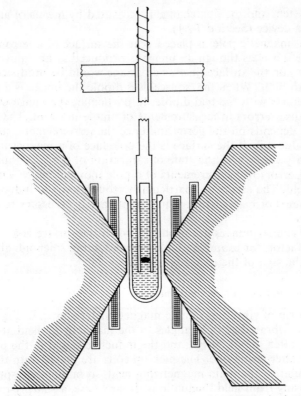

**Figure 7.12**   Induction method for measurement of magnetization.

system, the time integral $\int e \, dt$ of which is equal to the flux $\Phi$ produced by the dipole. The flux is a measure of the dipole moment and thus of the magnetization of the specimen. The pick-up coils can be located inside a solenoid or other source of field so that the moment can be measured as a function of externally applied field.

Ideally changes in the magnetizing field should not contribute to the measured flux change. Unfortunately it is impossible to design a practical coil system which prevents this. Usually a secondary pick-up coil is connected in series opposition to the first, so placed that it senses changes in the magnetizing field but not in the effect of the dipole. By adjusting the relative contributions of the two, fairly good compensation can be achieved. The design of good pick-up coils is complicated.

An experimental arrangement using this method is shown schematically in Fig. 7.12. The specimen is withdrawn mechanically from the coil system and the flux change is measured by means of an integrating device (Section 7.2.1).

When a 'magnetic pole' is placed near the surface of a ferromagnetic body the effect is as though an image is produced at an equivalent position inside the surface, just as an image would be produced in a mirror with light. When the 'source' is a dipole the image is a dipole which interacts with the real dipole. In particular, the image when present causes errors in measurements of dipole moment. The strength of the image depends on the permeability of the ferromagnetic surface which produces it. If the surface is the pole face of a magnet its permeability varies with the state of saturation of the face, thus producing errors in measurements of dipole moment which vary with applied field. The errors are particularly troublesome in induction measurements of magnetization and great care is necessary to eliminate them.

Exactly similar images are produced when the surface is a superconductor, for example in a superconducting solenoid, although in this case the sign of the image is reversed.

### 7.3.2  *Vibrating-sample magnetometer*

In the form of vibrating-sample magnetometer shown in Fig. 7.13 the specimen is vibrated at right angles to the magnetizing field at a fixed frequency, often about 80 Hz, and the inductive signal in the pick-up coils is an alternating one. The pick-up coils are placed with their axes perpendicular to the main magnetizing field, so minimizing spurious signals arising from field fluctuations. In any case, a sharply-tuned signal-detecting system reduces unwanted background signals to a very low level. The transmission of spurious vibrations at the measured frequency must be carefully avoided.

The usual method is to attach a small permanent magnet to a remote part of the vibrating system. This moves inside its own pick-up coils and provides a reference signal against which the signal produced by the sample can be measured accurately.

This method of measuring magnetization is a relatively sensitive one.

### 7.3.3  *The force method*

The force acting on a magnetizable specimen situated in a (non-uniform) magnetic field may be calculated from the variation of its free energy with position. When the magnetization is uniform throughout the specimen and the field varies with position the force is given by

$$F = -V\boldsymbol{M}.\nabla\boldsymbol{B}_0 = -m\boldsymbol{\sigma}.\nabla\boldsymbol{B}_0 \tag{7.43}$$

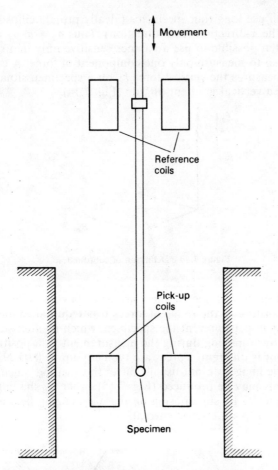

**Figure 7.13**   Vibrating-sample magnetometer.

where $V$ and $m$ are the volume and the mass of the specimen respectively. Writing Equ. 7.43 in its Cartesian component form we have (neglecting the negative sign)

$$
\begin{aligned}
(1/m)|F_x| &= \sigma_x \partial B_0^x/\partial x + \sigma_y \partial B_0^y/\partial x + \sigma_z \partial B_0^z/\partial x \\
(1/m)|F_y| &= \sigma_x \partial B_0^x/\partial y + \sigma_y \partial B_0^y/\partial y + \sigma_z \partial B_0^z/\partial y \\
(1/\dot{m})|F_z| &= \sigma_x \partial B_0^x/\partial z + \sigma_y \partial B_0^y/\partial z + \sigma_z \partial B_0^z/\partial z
\end{aligned}
\tag{7.44}
$$

The directions of $x$, $y$ and $z$ are shown in Fig. 7.14.

Various experimental arrangements simplify equations 7.44 in different ways. Nearly all use long thin specimens (ideally prolate ellipsoids) aligned along the $x$-direction (field direction). Thus $\sigma_x = \sigma$, $\sigma_y = 0$ and $\sigma_z = 0$. It is often possible to use a balance sensitive only in a single direction, and so to measure only one component of force. A commonly used method measures the vertical force $F_z$ on a specimen situated in a field $B_0^x$ having a vertical gradient $dB_0^x/dz$ (Fig. 7.14).

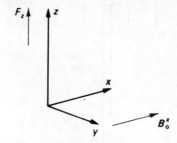

**Figure 7.14**   Definition of coordinates.

A number of different force balances are used, having different sensitivities according to the range of forces it is required to measure. The main problem is to prevent the specimen, which is often small (about 50 mg) from moving during the measurement to a position where the field gradient is different. Forces are typically up to 0·05 N (5000 dynes). Magnetic images do not usually affect this method much.

Field gradients may be produced (Fig. 7.15) either by shaping the pole tips of the magnet or by superposing on the magnetizing field a field gradient produced by an electric current.

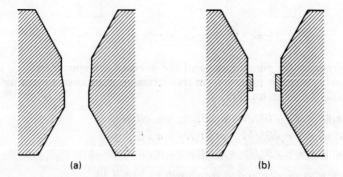

(a)                                 (b)

**Figure 7.15**   Production of field gradient: (a) shaped poles; (b) with parallel conductors.

Nearly all magnetization measurements by any method are made relatively to a standard specimen. In the force method this avoids having to measure field gradients accurately. Suitable materials are pure iron or pure nickel. Their magnetizations are given in Table 7.3.

**Table 7.3** Standards for calibrating measurements of magnetization and susceptibility.

| Material | Magnetization ($J\,T^{-1}\,kg^{-1} = erg\,Oe^{-1}\,g^{-1}$) at temperatures (K) | | |
|---|---|---|---|
| | 293 | 77 | 4 |
| Nickel | $55\cdot1\pm0\cdot1$ | $58\cdot4\pm0\cdot1$ | $58\cdot6\pm0\cdot1$ |
| Iron | $217\cdot6\pm0\cdot1$ | $221\cdot4\pm0\cdot1$ | $221\cdot7\pm0\cdot1$ |
| | Mass susceptibility ($J\,T^{-2}\,kg^{-1}\times10^{-2}$ or $erg\,Oe^{-2}\,g^{-1}\times10^{-6}$) at a temperature of 293 K | | |
| Tantalum | $0\cdot8490\pm0\cdot0006$ | | |
| Palladium | $5\cdot231\pm0\cdot004$ | | |

## 7.4 Measurement of paramagnetic susceptibility

The force method is the one which is used most in measuring paramagnetic susceptibility. The chief difference from Section 7.3.3 is that the forces are smaller and therefore greater sensitivity is required in the force measurement.

If we write $\sigma_x = \chi B_0^x$ in Equ. 7.44 we get

$$F_x = m\chi B_0^x \, dB_0^x/dz \tag{7.45}$$

The force is therefore greatest when $B_0^x \, dB_0^x/dz$ is at a maximum. In an electromagnet this is usually near the edge of the pole gap (Fig. 7.16).

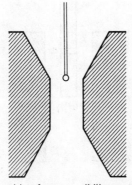

**Figure 7.16** Specimen position for susceptibility measurement by force method.

In this form this measurement is not absolute, since $B_0^x \, dB_0^x/dz$ is difficult to measure accurately. For relative measurements various standards are used depending on the range of sensitivity for which the balance is designed. Two of them are Ta and Pd, both in pure metallic form (see Table 7.3).

The Gouy method is a variant of the force method which permits absolute measurement of paramagnetic susceptibility in long, thin, uniform specimens that are absolutely free from ferromagnetic contamination.

For a uniform paramagnetic specimen, the vertical force on a small element of length $dz$ (Fig. 7.17) is

$$dF_z = dm \, \chi \, B_0^x \, dB_0^x/dz = \tfrac{1}{2}(\rho \, \alpha \, dz \, \chi) \, d(B_0^x)^2/dz \tag{7.46}$$

Thus

$$F_z = \tfrac{1}{2}\chi \, \alpha \, \rho((B_0^x)_1^2 - (B_0^x)_2^2) \tag{7.47}$$

Usually when the specimen length is adequate $(B_0^x)_2^2$ may be neglected. Since the area of cross section $\alpha$ and the density $\rho$ may usually be measured accurately, the susceptibility $\chi$ may be determined absolutely.

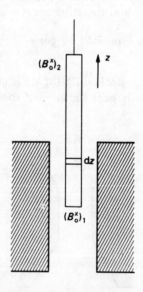

**Figure 7.17.** Gouy method.

### 7.4.1  *Effect of ferromagnetic impurities on the measurement of paramagnetic susceptibility*

The test for the presence of ferromagnetic contamination in a paramagnetic sample is to measure the apparent susceptibility $\chi_{app}$ in different field strengths. In a pure paramagnet the susceptibility is independent of field.

When a small fraction $x$ of a ferromagnetic impurity is present, the magnetization of which is $\sigma$ per unit mass the apparent susceptibility of the whole specimen is

$$\chi_{app} = (1-x)\chi + x\sigma/B_0 \qquad (7.48)$$

where $\chi$ is the true susceptibility of the paramagnetic component. Thus a graph should be plotted of $\chi_{app}$ against $(B_0)^{-1}$. The true susceptibility is indicated by the intercept at $(B_0)^{-1} = 0$, since $(1-x)$ rarely differs much from unity.

This correction will not work for the Gouy method, since different parts of the specimen are situated in different but undefined fields. Nor will it work for superparamagnets, for which the apparent susceptibility depends to some extent on the field.


## 7.5  Derivation of spontaneous magnetization from experimental data

A typical set of experimental data for the dependence of magnetization on field at different temperatures is shown in Fig. 1.3. If the measured magnetization is essentially independent of field at low temperatures the measured values are certainly intrinsic. The linear extrapolation to where the internal field (applied field corrected for demagnetizing field) is zero gives the value of the spontaneous magnetization for the temperature at which the measurements were made. The same procedure can then be followed at higher temperatures, still remote from the Curie temperature.

Near $T_C$ the isothermal $(\sigma, B_0)$ graphs are curved and difficult to extrapolate to $B_0 = 0$. It is helpful to construct graphs of $B_0$ against $T$ for constant $\sigma$, by interpolation from a graph such as Fig. 1.3. More temperatures are required than are shown in Fig. 1.3. Fig. 7.18 shows such a set of curves of constant magnetization. The temperature for which the magnetization of a given line is the spontaneous magnetization is the extrapolation to where $B_0 = 0$. This is not strictly an exact procedure but it introduces little error for a homogeneous ferromagnet at temperatures within a few degrees of $T_C$ (so that $T/T_C < 0.98$). A better measurement uses the magnetocaloric effect, but this is slow and difficult.

At low temperatures ($T/T_C < 0.1$) the spontaneous magnetization is

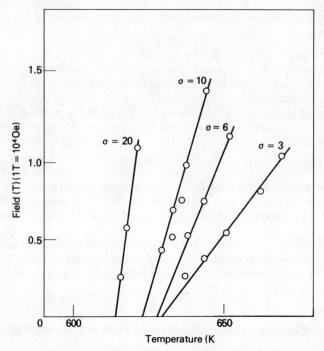

**Figure 7.18**  Curves of constant magnetization for nickel.

expected from spin-wave theory to vary according to the law

$$\sigma_T/\sigma_0 = 1 - A(T/T_C)^{3/2} \tag{7.49}$$

where $A$ is a constant of proportionality. Thus the saturation magnetic
moment, the value of the spontaneous magnetization at zero
temperature, is obtained by plotting graphs of the spontaneous
magnetization against $T^{3/2}$ and extrapolating them to where $T = 0$. This
is useful if the lowest temperature of measurement is not higher than
$0.05\ T_C$.

When the measured magnetization varies markedly with field at all
temperatures it is not at all clear that it is the intrinsic magnetization
that is being measured. The variation of magnetization with field might
be due to domain effects and the interpretation is more difficult. If no
better information is available an approximation to the zero temperature
saturation magnetization can sometimes be obtained by extrapolating
the measured magnetization to its value for $(B_0)^{-1} = 0$ at each
temperature, and then extrapolating these values against $T^{3/2}$ or $T^2$ to
$T = 0$.

## 7.6   Measurement of Curie temperature

The Curie temperature of a ferromagnet is not obviously identified in a superficial examination of the results of magnetization measurements, because of the disturbing influence of the field which must be applied to align the domains. Strictly speaking, a sharp second-order phase transition only exists when there is no field. The procedure which follows is called either the Arrott method or the Belov and Goryaga method.

Near the Curie temperature the reduced magnetization $\sigma_{B,T}/\sigma_{0,0}$ is fairly small. It is argued that under these conditions differences in the applicability of different models of ferromagnetism are not great and it is sufficient to adapt the simple theory of a local-moment ferromagnet. Here the quantities analogous to the molecular field coefficient ($\gamma$) and the atomic magnetic moment ($\mu$) have no necessary exact significance, being more of the nature of empirical constants. Adapting equations 2.8 and 2.6 (with $J = \frac{1}{2}$) we write

$$\sigma_{B,T}/\sigma_{0,0} = \tanh[(B_0 + \gamma\sigma_{B,T})\mu/kT] \tag{7.50}$$

Thus

$$(B_0 + \gamma\sigma_{B,T})\mu/kT = \tanh^{-1}(\sigma_{B,T}/\sigma_{0,0})$$
$$= (\sigma_{B,T}/\sigma_{0,0}) + \tfrac{1}{3}(\sigma_{B,T}/\sigma_{0,0})^3 + \tfrac{1}{5}(\sigma_{B,T}/\sigma_{0,0})^5 \ldots \tag{7.51}$$

which tends to $(\sigma_{B,T}/\sigma_{0,0})$ when $T \to T_C$. That is,

$$T = \frac{\mu\sigma_{0,0}}{k}\left(\frac{B_0}{\sigma_{B,T}} + \gamma\right) \tag{7.52}$$

At $T = T_C$ the reciprocal of the susceptibility $(B_0/\sigma_{B,T})$ is zero or very small. Thus

$$\gamma = kT_C/\mu\sigma_{0,0} \tag{7.53}$$

For temperatures near but not necessarily equal to $T_C$

$$\mu B_0/kT = (\sigma_{B,T}/\sigma_{0,0}) - (\sigma_{B,T}/\sigma_{0,0})T_C/T + \tfrac{1}{3}(\sigma_{B,T}/\sigma_{0,0})^3$$

or,

$$(B_0/\sigma_{B,T}) = (kT/3\mu\sigma_{0,0}^3)\sigma_{B,T}^2 + (k/\mu\sigma_{0,0})(T - T_C) \tag{7.54}$$
$$= AT\sigma_{B,T}^2 + C(T - T_C) \tag{7.55}$$

where $A$ and $C$ are constants characteristic of the material.

Thus we expect graphs of $(B_0/\sigma_{B,T})$ against $\sigma_{B,T}^2$ at constant temperature to be linear. Their intercept on the axis, where $\sigma_{B,T}^2 = 0$, gives

$$(B_0/\sigma_{B,T})_0 = C(T - T_C) \tag{7.56}$$

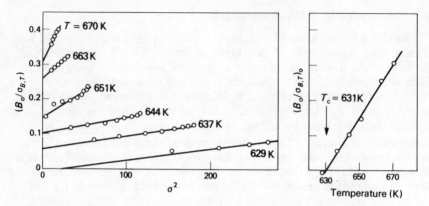

**Figure 7.19**   Procedure for determination of Curie temperature.

which varies linearly with $T$, having a zero value when $T = T_C$. Fig. 7.19 illustrates the procedure.

The method may only be used fairly close to $T_C$ and in fields which are not too high, or the conditions of the approximations will not hold. Also, it is not applicable to heterogeneous systems having more than a single Curie temperature.

A rough approximation to the Curie temperature which is good enough for many purposes can be measured quite simply. The magnetization is measured as a function of temperature in a constant field (say of the order of 0·2 T, or 2000 Oe). Where the graph of magnetization against temperature goes through a point of inflexion is usually within a range of $\pm 10$ K of the true Curie temperature.

# 8

# Applications of Magnetism

Applications of magnetism are of two main kinds. There are applications of magnetic properties and magnetic measuring techniques to problems in wider areas, such as metallurgy or in chemistry. Or there are the uses of the magnetic properties of materials to provide devices of wide applicability. Examples under both headings are given in this chapter. Other examples may be found in the literature. The important applications of magnetic resonance to chemistry and to the study of defects in solids are not described here (but see the book by Henderson in the present series).

## 8.1 Magnetic phase analysis of alloys

In constitutional studies of alloys that contain more than one phase it is often important to be able to measure the proportion of each phase present, or to determine the compositions of the phases. In favourable circumstances magnetic measurements may be used to obtain such information, often complementing the use of other techniques, for instance X-ray diffraction or metallography.

The intrinsic magnetization $\sigma_{B,T}$ of a ferromagnet is a unique function of field and temperature which is insensitive to experimental conditions and to the degree of mixing with other materials. So long as the field is strong enough to eliminate domain effects, variations of field have a small effect on the measured magnetization and it differs little from the spontaneous magnetization $\sigma_{0,T}$, except near $T_C$ (Fig. 1.3). The relationship between $\sigma_{0,T}$ and the temperature $T$ characterizes a material, or a composition within a solid solution. The dependence of $T_C$ on composition may be determined for a given phase from preliminary measurements under single-phase conditions. When the same phase is present in a multiphase alloy its composition may be found by measuring its Curie temperature. This procedure may be followed whether the other phases present are ferromagnetic or not, but there must be no possibility of confusion between their respective Curie temperatures.

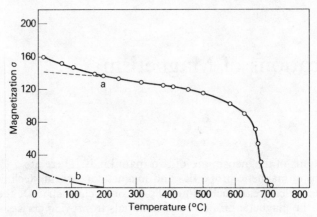

**Figure 8.1** Magnetic phase analysis of a two-phase iron–nickel alloy (after Hoselitz and Sucksmith, 1943, *Proc. R. Soc.* A, **181**, 307.)

An example of this is given in Fig. 8.1. The graph was obtained for a two-phase iron–nickel alloy containing an average of 16 % of nickel. The alloy consists of a body-centred cubic majority phase having a relatively high Curie temperature and a face-centred cubic minority phase, the Curie temperature of which is near 400 K. Measurements on single-phase f.c.c. FeNi alloys have shown that when $T_C = 400$ K the nickel content is close to 31 % by weight. Also, the spontaneous magnetization of this single-phase alloy at 273 K is 69·6 J $T^{-1}$ $kg^{-1}$ ( = erg $Oe^{-1}$ $g^{-1}$). The contribution from the f.c.c. phase (curve b of Fig. 8.1) to the magnetization of the two-phase alloy at 273 K is found experimentally to be about 20 J $T^{-1}$ $kg^{-1}$. Thus the fraction of the two-phase alloy which is f.c.c. phase is 20/69·6 = 0·29, and this must contain 0·31 × 0·29 = 0·090 of the nickel present. If the b.c.c. phase is the only other present its fraction must be 1 − 0·29 = 0·71, containing 0·16 − 0·090 = 0·07 of the total amount of nickel in the two-phase alloy. Thus the composition of the b.c.c. phase must be about 0·07/0·71 = 9·9 % of nickel by weight. The compositions of both phases present in this two-phase alloy are therefore known. This is a powerful method for studying suitable two-phase alloys when they are in equilibrium. It can give important information on the boundaries of mixed-phase regions in alloy equilibrium diagrams.

In general, in a multiphase alloy the observed dependence of spontaneous magnetization on temperature is the sum of the independent effects from all the separate phases, combined according to their proportions. In work of this kind it is usual to take the magnetization (per unit mass) measured in a single strong field as being sufficiently close to the spontaneous magnetization.

Let the measured (spontaneous) magnetization of the alloy at temperatures $T_1$, $T_2$, $T_3$, ... be $\sigma_1$, $\sigma_2$, $\sigma_3$, ... . Let us suppose that the phases present have been identified qualitatively and that their magnetic characteristics are capable of being established in a separate experiment. At the same temperatures the magnetization of one of the phases is $a_1$, $a_2$, $a_3$, ..., and so on for the other phases, giving $b_1$, $b_2$, $b_3$, ... $c_1$, $c_2$, $c_3$, ... . Let the respective fractions of these phases be $z$, $y$, $x$, ... . Then

$$a_1 z + b_1 y + c_1 x + ... = \sigma_1$$
$$a_2 z + b_2 y + c_2 x + ... = \sigma_2$$
$$a_3 z + b_3 y + c_3 x + ... = \sigma_3 \qquad (8.1)$$
$$\cdot$$
$$\cdot$$
$$\cdot$$
$$a_n z + b_n y + c_n x + ... = \sigma_n$$

Simultaneous solution of equations 8.1 now gives the proportions of the phases. The coefficient for one of the phases may have the value zero at all temperatures (that is, one phase can be non-magnetic), but if two or more of the phases have an identical dependence of magnetization on temperature, their proportions will appear lumped together in the final result. Otherwise the result is unique.

The sensitivity of the analysis is greatest when the temperatures are chosen so as to emphasize the differences between the phases. The first temperature should be as low as possible and the others in increasing order, respectively just above the Curie temperature of each phase. Analysis by this method is simplest when the ferromagnetic phases involved are of fixed composition, although this is not essential. However, the dependence of spontaneous magnetization on temperature for the phases and compositions actually present must be known accurately.

Fig. 8.2 illustrates the application of magnetic phase analysis to an iron–carbon alloy. As a result of chemical analysis the specimen was known to contain 1·73 % of carbon by weight, and to be free from significant impurities. In its annealed state it consisted of body-centred cubic iron having a very small amount of carbon in solid solution (called ferrite) and a precipitated iron carbide $Fe_3C$ (called cementite). Both phases are ferromagnetic and the $(\sigma, T)$ graph of the alloy is as shown in Fig. 8.2. The $(\sigma, T)$ graphs of Fe and $Fe_3C$ are also shown. Application and solution of equations 8.1 showed that the fraction of $Fe_3C$ present was 0·262 and the fraction of Fe was 0·769. The difference between the sum of these two fractions and unity is a measure of the error inherent in the analysis. The full line which joins the experimental points in Fig. 8.2 was calculated from the result of the analysis. Since $Fe_3C$ contains 6·69 %

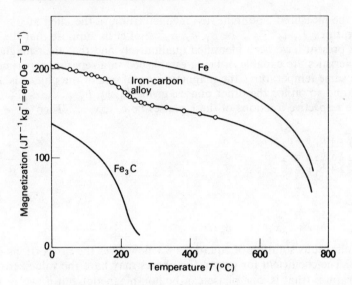

**Figure 8.2**   Magnetic phase analysis of an iron-carbon alloy.

of carbon by weight, the indicated composition is $6 \cdot 69 \times 0 \cdot 262 = 1 \cdot 75 \%$ by weight, agreeing well with the chemical analysis.

A similar method of magnetic analysis is possible in the paramagnetic state. However, it is only applicable when there are no more than two phases, and these must have known and widely differing susceptibilities. One application is the measurement of the amounts of the b.c.c. and f.c.c. phases in iron-rich binary alloys at high temperatures.

In pure iron at temperatures above the Curie temperature the $\alpha$-phase (body-centred cubic) and the $\gamma$-phase (face-centred cubic) are both paramagnetic and their susceptibilities differ widely. This difference is often maintained when other elements are dissolved in iron in binary alloys. It forms the basis of a method for determining the boundaries of the $\gamma$-loop regions in the equilibrium diagrams of such alloy systems.

In two-phase alloys where both phases are paramagnetic the susceptibility of each phase acts independently. At a given temperature the mass susceptibility $\chi$ of a mixture of the $\gamma$- and $\alpha$-phases is given by

$$\chi = y\chi_\gamma + (1-y)\chi_\alpha \tag{8.2}$$

where $y$ is the proportion by weight of $\gamma$-phase present and $\chi_\gamma$ and $\chi_\alpha$ refer to the $\gamma$- and the $\alpha$-phases respectively at the temperature chosen. $\chi_\gamma$ and $\chi_\alpha$ are not independent of temperature, but they vary smoothly in a way which allows extrapolation from single-phase conditions to temperatures where mixed phases exist. Thus the proportions of the two phases present in a given state may be estimated quantitatively.

The example given here is of the application of this method to the determination of the boundaries of the $\gamma$-loop in the equilibrium diagram of the FeSi alloy system.

Usually the $\alpha$- to $\gamma$-phase change shows marked temperature hysteresis. The course of the graph showing the proportion of $\gamma$-phase as a function of temperature for this transformation would depend on whether the susceptibility was measured during heating or cooling, and also on the rate of change of temperature (see Fig. 8.3). The graph for equilibrium conditions, corresponding to an infinitely slow rate, would lie somewhere between those for heating and cooling. The following method allows equilibrium conditions to be recognized.

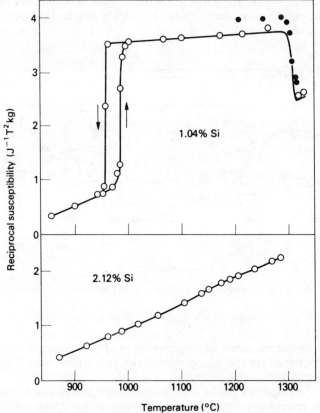

**Figure 8.3**  Reciprocal susceptibility plotted against temperature for two iron–silicon alloys.

If a specimen is heated from a low temperature into the region of the phase transformation and then the heating process is halted, the specimen will be in a non-equilibrium two-phase state possessing less $\gamma$-phase than the equilibrium amount. If it is then cooled slowly at a constant rate the tendency will be for the amount of $\gamma$-phase to continue to increase at a diminishing rate until the temperature has been reached at which the proportions of phases present are in equilibrium, after which it will decrease. When the amounts of $\gamma$-phase present during this slow cooling are plotted on a graph against temperature, the maximum of the line obtained represents a point on another graph of the equilibrium proportions of phases against temperature. The procedure may be repeated for a series of different initial states. The equilibrium graph for each alloy is given by the locus of the maxima of the curves obtained. A similar procedure may be applied starting from states containing more $\gamma$-phase than the equilibrium amount and then slowly-heating the specimen. The method is illustrated in Fig. 8.4.

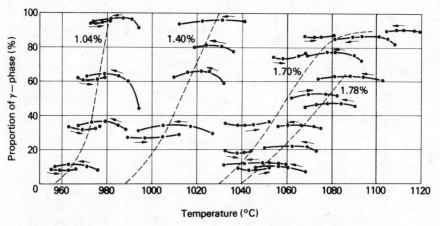

**Figure 8.4**   Method of recognizing phase equilibrium in analysis of iron–silicon alloys.

Phase boundaries may also be located roughly by observing discontinuities in the variation of susceptibility with temperature.

The result obtained for the $\gamma$-loop part of the FeSi equilibrium diagram is shown in Fig. 8.5.

This general method is a useful tool in suitable circumstances but it is rather severely restricted in the kind of problem to which it may be applied. It has been used to study martensitic transformations in steels.

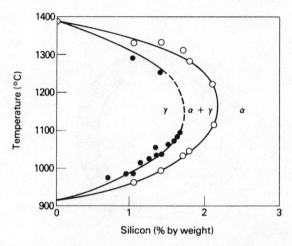

**Figure 8.5**  $\gamma$-loop in the iron–silicon phase diagram.

## 8.2   Permanent magnets

Examples of device applications of permanent magnets are:
electric motors of low power
electric generators
moving coil meters
loudspeakers
magnetic separators
control devices for electron beams
magnetic holding applications.

Each application creates its own problems of design and quite often differing materials are used for different kinds of application. Sometimes the aim is to maximize the scientific performance. But many applications are of a mass production nature and a commercial compromise is necessary to balance a conflict between tolerable scientific properties and acceptable cost.

### 8.2.1   *Energy associated with a magnetic field*

Consider a toroidal coil (Fig. 8.6) having $N$ turns, mean circumference $l$ and area of cross section $A$, and let an increasing current be supplied. A back EMF will be induced in the coil proportional to the rate of change of flux $\Phi$ enclosed. While the current is changing, work is being done at the rate

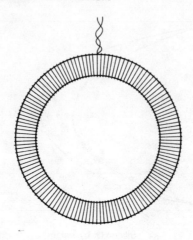

**Figure 8.6**    Toroidal coil.

$$dW/dt = i(N\,d\Phi/dt) = i(N\,A\,dB/dt) \tag{8.3}$$

where $B$ is the induction within the coil.

Since the magnetic excitation $H$ produced by the current is

$$H = iN/l \tag{8.4}$$

Equ. 8.3 becomes

$$dW/dt = (iN/l)A\,l\,dB/dt = H\,V\,dB/dt \tag{8.5}$$

where $V = A\,l$ is the volume enclosed by the coil. Thus the energy involved in setting up a field $B_0$ is

$$W = (V/\mu_0) \int B_0\,dB \tag{8.6}$$

In free space $\mu_r = 1$, $B = B_0$, and

$$W = V B_0^2/2\mu_0 = \tfrac{1}{2} V B_0 H \tag{8.7}$$

The energy per unit volume in a field in free space is

$$E = \tfrac{1}{2}B_0^2/\mu_0 = \tfrac{1}{2}B_0 H\,\mathrm{J\,m^{-3}}\ (\text{in SI units, or }\mathrm{erg\,cm^{-3}}\text{ in CGS units}) \tag{8.8}$$

### 8.2.2    *Energy of a permanent magnet*

Let us consider now the ring-shaped permanent magnet shown in

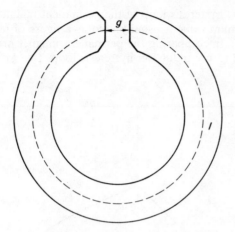

**Figure 8.7**    Ring-shaped permanent magnet.

Fig. 8.7. If there are no electric currents we may write, for the whole magnetic circuit (see Equ. 7.15)

$$\oint \boldsymbol{H}.\mathrm{d}\boldsymbol{l} = 0 \tag{8.9}$$

In a perfect system free from magnetic leakage and where the field is everywhere uniform

$$H_g g + H_m l = 0 \tag{8.10}$$

where $H_g\,(= (B_0)_g/\mu_0)$ and $H_m\,(= (B_0)^m/\mu_0)$ are respectively the magnetic excitations in the gap and in the magnet. Across the gap the flux must be continuous:

$$B_g A_g = B_m A_m \tag{8.11}$$

where $A_g$ and $A_m$ are the areas of cross section of gap and magnet respectively. Thus $H_g g B_g A_g = -H_m l B_m A_m$, or

$$\tfrac{1}{2} B_g H_g V_g = -\tfrac{1}{2} B_m H_m V_m \tag{8.12}$$

where $V_g$ and $V_m$ are respectively the volumes of gap and magnet.

The left-hand side of Equ. 8.12 is the magnetic energy stored in the gap of the magnet (see Equ. 8.8). Apart from the geometrical relationship between $V_g$ and $V_m$ this is given by half the product

$$B_m H_m = (1/\mu_0) B_m (B_0)_m \tag{8.13}$$

The product is called the energy product of the magnet. It varies between different parts of the hysteresis loop of the permanent magnet material (Fig. 8.8). Its maximum value is usually used as a figure of merit for the material (Table 8.1). In comparing the permanent magnet properties of materials it is usual to use induction hysteresis loops (see §1.1.1 and Fig. 1.1b).

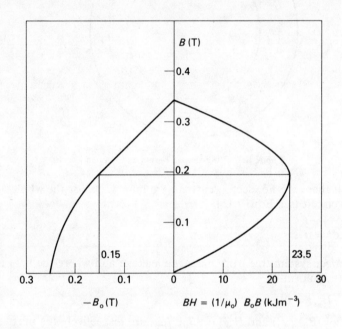

**Figure 8.8** Second quadrant of hysteresis loop of barium ferrite, and the dependence of the energy product on the induction $B$.

**Table 8.1** Characteristics of some permanent-magnet materials.

| Material | Induction coercivity (T) | Remanent induction (T) | $(BH)_{max}$ (kJ m$^{-3}$) |
|---|---|---|---|
| Alnico | 0·1 | 0·8 | 25 |
| Alcomax | 0·07 | 1·25 | 44 |
| Barium ferrite | 0·25 | 0·35 | 24 |
| MnBi | 0·37 | 0·48 | 44 |
| SmCo$_5$ | 0·85 | 0·9 | 160 |
| PtCo | 0·48 | 0·64 | 74 |

The working condition of a permanent magnet is set by its demagnetizing field (see §6.4 and Fig. 6.14) and this depends mostly on the geometry of the magnet. Writing $\mu_0 H_g = (B_0)_g$ in Equ. 8.12 and $B_g = (B_0)_g$ for the air gap in which the relative permeability $\mu_r$ is effectively unity

$$(1/\mu_0)(B_0)_g^2 = -(B_m H_m) V_m/V_g \qquad (8.14)$$

To obtain the highest field in the gap the energy product of the magnet must therefore have its maximum value. If the volume of the air gap is predetermined the designer of the magnet must select a material and a magnet shape so that the magnet works near $(BH)_{max}$. This is not always straightforward, partly due to several complicating factors which we have ignored here.

In many applications the stability of the field produced by a permanent magnet is important. Since the spontaneous magnetization varies with temperature so must the induction and thus the field produced in the air gap. One consequence is that the sensitivity of moving-coil meters is not altogether independent of the ambient temperature. Another is that the torque of motors incorporating permanent magnets falls as the working temperature rises. It is therefore desirable that permanent magnet materials should have Curie temperatures as high as possible.

## 8.3  Applications of soft magnetic materials

Soft magnetic materials are used widely as cores for transformers and inductors. The properties required in a soft magnetic material are a small coercivity, a large saturation magnetization, large initial and maximum permeability and a small hysteresis loss. To some extent these requirements conflict and the selection of material for a given application is a compromise. Table 8.2 summarizes some of the properties available.

**Table 8.2**  Properties of some soft magnetic materials.

| Material | Induction coercivity (T) | Maximum permeability (T) | Remanent induction (T) |
| --- | --- | --- | --- |
| Pure iron | $10^{-6}$ | 350000 | 2·2 |
| Silicon iron | $1·5 \times 10^{-5}$ | 40000 | 2·0 |
| Supermalloy | $4 \times 10^{-7}$ | $10^6$ | 0·8 |
| MnZn ferrite | $3 \times 10^{-5}$ | 5000 | 0·3 |

Almost all the devices used in the generation, distribution and large scale use of electrical power depend on the use of FeSi alloys. Power supplies are nearly always alternating and the supply frequency is almost universally either 50 Hz or 60 Hz. The material of the magnetic circuits in transformers, generators and motors therefore carries an alternating flux and this produces eddy currents when the material is metallic. These are a source of energy loss. Non-metallic materials are not generally suitable for these applications because their saturation induction (flux density) is too low.

Because of eddy currents the magnetic flux tends to concentrate near the surface of the magnetic material, leading to poor magnetic utilization of the material as well as energy loss due to the eddy currents themselves. These effects get worse at higher frequencies. Magnetic circuits working at about 50 Hz and employing silicon iron are usually built of laminations typically about 0·33 mm (0·013 in) thick having a thin surface coating of insulation. Skin effects are thereby minimized and the induction is nearly uniform across the thickness of the laminations.

The addition of silicon to iron is beneficial for several reasons. The most important is that it increases the electrical resistivity considerably, reducing eddy current effects. Also, the magnetocrystalline anisotropy is reduced, leading to easier movement of domain boundary walls. Another reason is that more than 2% of silicon (see Fig. 8.5) suppresses the formation of the f.c.c. $\gamma$-phase at high temperatures. Annealing processes aimed at promoting grain growth during the preparation of grain-oriented material can take place wholly within the b.c.c. $\alpha$-phase. There is no destructive $\gamma$- to $\alpha$-phase transformation on cooling.

Commercial silicon iron sheet often has a grain size of several millimeteres and in the best material more than 90% of the grains are oriented within a few degrees of having a (110) plane in the plane of the sheet and a [001] easy direction along the length of the sheet. Such material has an induction of about 1·8 T (18 000 G) in a field of $10^{-3}$ T (10 Oe). The total rate of energy loss of such material when in use in the form of standard laminations is typically about 1 W kg$^{-1}$.

One application of the group of materials based on nickel–iron alloys is in magnetic screening, useful for protecting various electronic components (for example television tubes) from the effects of stray magnetic fields. Here the property that is required is that the induction shall be as large as possible in a very small field, in order that as much flux as possible shall be carried within the body of the screening material. That is, a relative permeability $\mu_r$ is required that is as large as possible in small fields. Some alloys reach an induction $B$ of about 0·6 T (6000 G) in a field of $2 \times 10^{-6}$ T ($2 \times 10^{-2}$ Oe). That the saturation induction is little greater than this value is relatively unimportant since it is often possible to increase the flux that can be carried by the screen by making it thicker.

When inductors or transformers having cores of magnetic materials are required to work at high frequencies, only non-metallic magnetic materials may be used. This generally means soft ferrites. Different materials are chosen for different kinds of application.

Ferrite-cored inductors are used as elements in frequency-selective circuits in a wide variety of electronic equipment. In carrier telephony especially, the performance and stability of such components is critical, in order that the resonant frequency of a circuit shall not wander with changes in ambient conditions. The form of a ferrite pot core inductor is shown in Fig. 8.9. The windings of the coil occupy the central spaces. This form is chosen so as to minimize magnetic coupling between adjacent components in an electrical circuit. The purpose of the magnetic shunt placed centrally is to allow the inductor to be adjusted to a required value of inductance. High-quality cored inductors are usually operated at very low amplitudes of field, thus avoiding hysteresis and other non-linear effects.

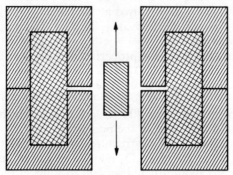

**Figure 8.9**  Ferrite pot core inductor.

Another application of soft ferrites is in making ferrite antennae for radio receivers. Almost all broadcast receivers using amplitude modulation that are now manufactured are provided with internal ferrite rod antennae. A short circular coil of $N$ turns enclosing an area $A$ is placed with its axis parallel to the magnetic field vector of the alternating signal being received. The aperture of the winding is filled with a relatively long ferrite cylinder of relative permeability $\mu_r$. It is coaxial with the coil and its centre coincides with the centre of the coil. The EMF $E$ induced in the coil is given by

$$E = E_0 \mu_r (2\pi A N/\lambda) \tag{8.15}$$

where $\lambda$ is the wavelength (in metres) and $E_0$ is the electric field strength of the signal being received. For a material selected to work at 1 MHz, $\mu_r$ might be about 1000. For another chosen to work at 30 MHz, $\mu_r$ is nearer to 100.

## 8.4   Magnetic tape recording

Magnetic tapes are used for the long-term storage of information. The magnetic material with which the tape is coated remembers its previous state of magnetization and the stored information may be retrieved subsequently by a reading process. There are two basically different kinds of operation. In computing, the level of the stored signal is relatively unimportant since it is only necessary to distinguish between binary code signals 0 or 1. However, writing and reading takes place at high speed. When speech is being recorded the signal level is important and little distortion is acceptable. For the recording of music the absence of distortion is especially important. In audio applications the speeds of writing and reading are relatively slow.

A magnetic tape consists of a tape made of a plastic material on to which is stuck a magnetic powder embedded in a plastic matrix. The magnetic material which is mostly used at the present time in commercial tapes is gamma ferric oxide ($\gamma$-$Fe_2O_3$). The particles of the powder are needle-shaped.

In order to discuss the magnetic properties of $\gamma$-$Fe_2O_3$ we start with another iron oxide, magnetite $Fe_3O_4$. This is a ferrimagnetic inverse spinel of the type described in Section 4.4.1. When $Fe_3O_4$ is heated in an oxidizing atmosphere, $\gamma$-$Fe_2O_3$ is formed. This is unstable and transforms on heating to temperatures above 400 °C to $\alpha$-$Fe_2O_3$, which is antiferromagnetic and unwanted in the present context.

$\gamma$-$Fe_2O_3$ is ferrimagnetic and its structure can be considered as a defect inverse spinel. The oxidation of $Fe_3O_4$ may be seen as an introduction of vacancies preferentially in an ordered way on to some of the spinel B-sites in place of some of the iron, thereby increasing the O/Fe ratio. The magnetic moment of $\gamma$-$Fe_2O_3$ is 2·5 $\mu_B$ per $Fe_2O_3$ molecule, compared with 4 $\mu_B$ per molecule for $Fe_3O_4$. The Curie temperature of $\gamma$-$Fe_2O_3$ is about 90 K higher than that of $Fe_3O_4$.

The shape of the particles of magnetite from which $\gamma$-$Fe_2O_3$ is produced controls the shape of the final particles, and this depends on which of two methods are used to prepare the magnetite. The two shapes have distinctly different magnetic properties. Most tapes contain single-domain acicular particles oriented in the direction of motion of the tape. They are typically about $\frac{1}{2}$ $\mu$m long with a length/width ratio of between 5 and 10. It is shape anisotropy which controls their magnetization characteristics. The coercivity of tape material is of the order of $2·5 \times 10^{-2}$ T (250 Oe).

What is of interest for recording purposes is how the minor-loop remanent magnetization varies with the maximum field previously applied. Such a relationship is shown in Fig. 8.10, for static applied fields.

Let us now consider how information may be written on a tape. The

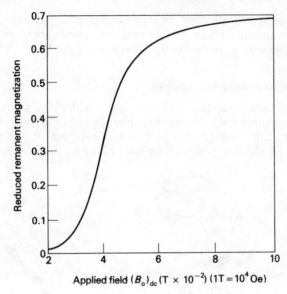

**Figure 8.10** Dependence of minor-loop remanent magnetization on the maximum field previously applied for $\gamma$-$Fe_2O_3$ in static fields. (After Mee, 1964, *Physics of Magnetic Recording*, North Holland, p. 190.)

tape is driven at constant velocity, rather less than 5 cm s$^{-1}$, with its plastic base in contact with a series of transducers. Each transducer (Fig. 8.11) consists of a magnetic ring of high permeability having a coil wound round it. The coil is used either to magnetize the ring when writing or to detect changes in the flux in the ring when reading. The leakage field at the gap in the ring writes on the tape. So that the greatest possible amount of information may be stored on the tape the gap is as narrow as possible. The first transducer erases any previous signal on the tape by applying a high-frequency alternating signal, the second writes and the third reads.

If the signal being recorded were simply applied to the writing transducer the remanent magnetization written on the tape would be far from a linear function of the applied field, as Fig. 8.10 shows. It is usually necessary to introduce some method of restoring linearity. The most common method is to mix the signal field with a bias field consisting of an alternating signal of high frequency and of an optimum amplitude. The bias field does not remain written on the tape. The remanent signal that does appear on the tape can be made proportional to the magnetizing signal to a fairly high degree, so long as the signal amplitude is not so great as to approach saturation.

Differing tape speeds are used for different signal frequencies. Video recording of frequencies up to 3 MHz uses tape speeds about one hundred times greater than those normally used for audio recording.

## 8.5   Applications of magnetic bubbles

The chief potential application of magnetic bubbles is in providing compact and versatile data storage for computing. At the time of writing no bubble data stores are yet in regular use in computers being produced commercially. Evaluation and proving are still taking place under test conditions.

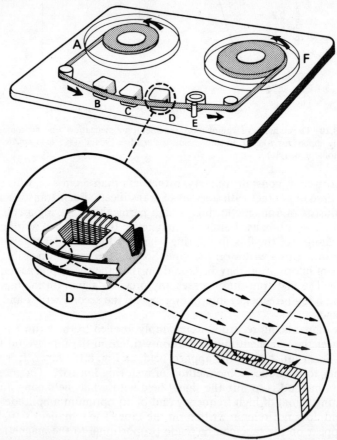

**Figure 8.11**   Writing on and reading from magnetic tapes. (After Mee, 1964, *Physics of Magnetic Recording*, North Holland, p. 3.)

In Section 6.5 we saw how bubble domains may be produced in thin uniaxial magnetic films having their easy direction of magnetization normal to the plane of the film. Now the aim is to indicate how bubbles may be used in technical devices. This is a field in which rapid development is taking place and technical details are likely to change quite quickly.

The physical characteristics required in the material in which bubbles are to be produced are quite critical. For stable bubbles to form their magnetization must be accurately perpendicular to the plane of the film. For this to occur the uniaxial magnetocrystalline anisotropy energy $K_u$ must be significantly greater than the magnetostatic energy given by $\frac{1}{2}\mu_0 M_s^2$, where $M_s$ is the saturation magnetization. A quality factor $Q$ is often used for bubble materials which expresses the ratio of these two energies:

$$Q = 2\mu_0 K_u/(\mu_0 M)^2 \tag{8.16}$$

Its value is typically about 5. Also for stability, the bubble length (equal to the film thickness) must not be significantly greater than the bubble diameter and this is usually a few micrometres. The domain wall thickness is of the order of 0·1 $\mu$m.

Another important parameter is called the characteristic length $\lambda$. Bubble formation depends on the ratio $\lambda/h$, where $h$ is the film thickness. Bubble diameters are usually of the order of 10$\lambda$. $\lambda$ depends on the intrinsic properties of the bubble material, in particular being proportional to $Q^{\frac{1}{2}}/M_s$. Calculated and measured values of $\lambda$ only agree roughly. Usual values are about 0·1 $\mu$m.

Materials which satisfy all these criteria are garnets, such as substituted YIG of the type $(EuY)_3(GaFe)_5O_{12}$ (see §4.4.7). Suitably oriented single-crystal films are grown epitaxially. There is a variety of techniques and liquid-phase epitaxy is commonly used. A non-magnetic substrate having the correct structure and lattice parameter is selected and oriented. Gadolinium gallium garnet $Gd_3Ga_5O_{12}$ is often used. The substrate is dipped for a controlled time into a flux solution of the correct composition held near saturation conditions at high temperature. An epitaxial film of the solute crystal grows on the surface of the substrate, from which it can subsequently be removed.

Having considered the medium in which bubbles may be formed we must now consider how they may be controlled usefully in the medium. The first requirement is a track along which bubbles may be moved and stored. Several types of track are possible but we consider only one.

It was shown in Section 6.5 that a bias field must always be applied normal to the film in order that bubbles may be formed at all. A pattern of T and I bars made of soft magnetic material is deposited on the surface

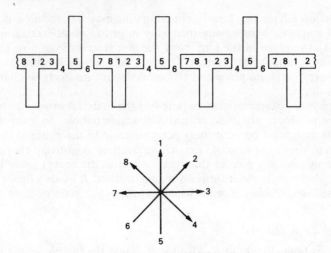

**Figure 8.12**   Magnetic overlay track made of T and I bars, illustrating method of bubble-domain transmission. (After O'Dell, 1974, *Magnetic Bubbles*, MacMillan, p. 133.)

of the garnet by evaporation, as in Fig. 8.12. The material is usually an alloy of composition near $Ni_3Fe$, similar to permalloy. The width of the bars is of the order of half the bubble diameter and their length is about five times their width, say about 15 $\mu$m. The bar thickness is not very important, but it is often about $0.1$ $\mu$m.

When the overlay is magnetized by superimposing a driving field in the plane of the film, the stray fields round the bars provide potential wells in which bubbles may be held. Rotating the driving field within the plane of the surface changes the position of the potential wells and thus provides the means of moving the bubbles in a controlled way. Referring to Fig. 8.12, let the polarities be such that when the drive field is in direction 1 the bubble is attracted to location 1, the upright of the T being magnetized along its length. Rotating the field clockwise through directions 1 to 8 provides a sequence of stable locations 1 to 8, so driving the bubble towards the right, from the centre of one T to the centre of the next. Since the repeat distance of the overlay pattern is of the order of 25 $\mu$m, there are about 400 bubble locations per centimetre of track. When the track spacing is about 40 $\mu$m there are of the order of $10^4$ locations per $cm^2$ of garnet surface. Rotation of the driving field is achieved by the use of static coils having their axes perpendicular to each other and parallel to the film, with appropriate phase control of the currents in each. Maximum possible driving frequencies depend on the detailed form of the overlay pattern used, being as high as 500 kHz in some cases. Bubble velocities are a few metres per second. A location which holds a bubble counts as 1 in the computer binary register and an empty location counts as zero.

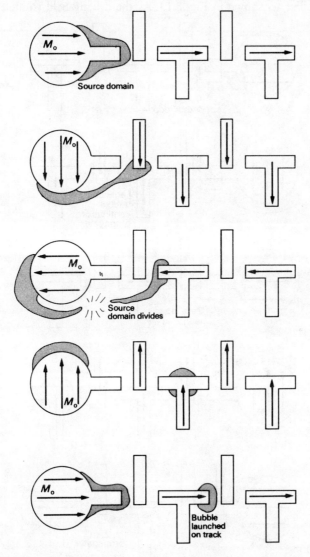

**Figure 8.13**   Injection of bubble domains. (After O'Dell, 1974, *Magnetic Bubbles*, MacMillan, p. 18.)

Bubble generation by the use of pulsed fields as outlined in Section 6.5 is difficult to operate and control when overlays are in use. A large and continuously replenished source domain is held by a relatively large permalloy disc, as shown in Fig. 8.13. As the driving field rotates, bubble

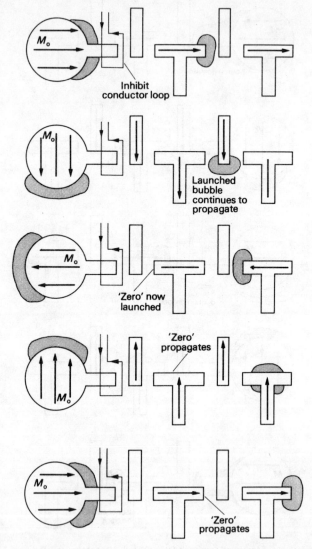

**Figure 8.14**    Injection of zero signal. (After O'Dell, 1974, *Magnetic Bubbles*, MacMillan, p. 19.)

domains break off as the diagram shows and they are injected into the track. When a zero is required to be injected a suitable conductor placed near the point of injection is energized. This prevents a bubble from being launched for chosen rotations of the drive field, as Fig. 8.14 shows.

Detection of bubbles is usually carried out using a suitably placed magnetoresistive sensor. The presence of a bubble may be detected from the stray field which it generates and the output from the sensor may be taken away as an electrical signal.

One of the most important advantages of this procedure is that there are no mechanical parts that might be subject to friction and wear.

# Further Reading and References

**General**
*Modern Magnetism.* L. F. Bates, Cambridge, 4th Edition 1961.
*Ferromagnetism.* R. M. Bozorth, Van Nostrand 1951.
*Physics of Magnetism.* S. Chikazumi, Wiley 1964.
*Magnetism in Solids.* D. H. Martin, Iliffe 1967.
*Physical Principles of Magnetism.* A. H. Morrish, Wiley 1965.
*Magnetism* (5 vols.). G. T. Rado and H. Suhl (Ed.), Academic Press 1963–75.

**Chapter 1** (Units in magnetism)
L. F. Bates. *Contemporary Physics*, **11**, 301, 1970.
J. Crangle. *Physics Bulletin*, **26**, 539, 1975.
A. E. Kennelly. *Proc. Instn. Elect. Engrs*, **78**, 35, 1936.
R. McWeeny. *Nature*, **243**, 196, 1973.
D. H. Smith. *Contemporary Physics*, **11**, 287, 1970.
*Lectures on Theoretical Physics*, A. Sommerfeld, Academic Press 1948.

**Chapter 2**
*Solid State Physics.* R. Kubo and T. Nagamiya (Ed.). McGraw Hill, English Edition 1969.
*Theory of Electric and Magnetic Susceptibilities.* J. H. Van Vleck, Oxford 1932.
*Introduction to the Theory of Magnetism.* D. Wagner (Translated by F. Cap), Pergamon 1972.

**Chapter 3**
E. C. Stoner, review in *Journal de Physique*, **12**, 372, 1951.
*Introduction to the Theory of Magnetism.* D. Wagner, Pergamon 1972.

**Chapter 4**
*Neutron Diffraction.* G. E. Bacon, Oxford 1962.
*The Magnetic Properties of Rare Earth Metals.* R. J. Elliott (Ed.). Plenum 1972.
T. Nagamiya, K. Yosida and R. Kubo, review in *Advances in Physics* **4**, 1, 1955.
L. Néel, *Annales de Physique* **3**, 154, 1948.

*Experimental Magnetochemistry.* M. M. Schieber, North Holland 1967.
*Effective Field Theories of Magnetism.* J. S. Smart, Saunders 1966.
*Ferrites.* J. Smit and H. P. J. Wijn, Philips (Cleaver-Hume) 1959.
*Physics of Rare Earth Solids.* K. N. R. Taylor and M. I. Darby, Chapman and Hall 1972.

## Chapter 5
P. W. Anderson, *Physical Review,* **80**, 922, 1950.
A. J. F. Boyle and H. E. Hall 'The Mössbauer effect' in *Rep. Prog. Physics* **25**, 441, 1962.
A. J. Freeman and R. E. Watson, 'Hyperfine interactions' in Rado and Suhl, *Magnetism* vol. 2A, Academic Press.
*Magnetism and the Chemical Bond.* J. B. Goodenough, Interscience 1963.
*Specific Heats at Low Temperatures.* E. S. R. Gopal, Heywood (Plenum) 1966.
W. Heisenberg, *Z. Physik.* **49**, 619, 1928.
W. Heitler and F. London, *Z. Physik,* **44**, 455, 1927.
*Theoretical Solid State Physics.* W. Jones and N. H. March, Wiley 1973.
H. A. Kramers, *Physica* **1**, 182, 1934.
*Theory of Magnetism.* D. C. Mattis, Harper and Row 1965.
M. A. Ruderman and C. Kittel, *Physical Review* **96**, 99, 1954.
*Principles of Magnetic Resonance.* C. P. Slichter, Harper and Row 1963.
*Introduction to the Theory of Magnetism.* D. Wagner, Pergamon, 1972.

## Chapter 6
*Ferromagnetism and Ferromagnetic Domains.* D. J. Craik and R. S. Tebble, North Holland 1965.
*Ferromagnetic Properties of Metals and Alloys.* K. Hoselitz, Oxford 1952.
*Magnetic Bubbles.* T. H. O'Dell, Macmillan 1974.
E. C. Stoner and E. P. Wohlfarth, *Phil. Trans. R. Soc.* **A240**, 599, 1948.
*Magnetic Materials.* R. S. Tebble and D. J. Craik, Wiley 1969.

## Chapter 7
*Construction of High Field Electromagnets.* D. De Klerk, Newport 1965.
*Experimental Methods in Magnetism* (2 vols.). H. Zijlstra, North Holland 1967.

## Chapter 8
*Magnetism and Metallurgy* (2 vols.). A. E. Berkowitz and E. Kneller (Ed.), Academic 1969.
*Physical Principles of Magnetism.* F. Brailsford, Van Nostrand 1966.
*Permanent Magnets and Magnetism.* D. Hadfield (Ed.), Iliffe 1962.
*Physics of Magnetic Recording.* C. D. Mee, North Holland 1964.
*Magnetic Bubbles.* T. H. O'Dell, Macmillan 1974.
*Soft Ferrites.* E. C. Snelling, Iliffe 1969.

# Index